The Great Yew Forest

The Great Yew Forest

the Natural History of Kingley Vale

Richard Williamson

M

To the memory of W. H. Hudson

The author and publishers would like to thank the following for supplying photographs:
J. Ashby pp. 97, 99; M. Boxall p. 104; Cambridge University Collection p.111 top; Roy A. Harris and K. R. Duff pp. 106, 107, 109, 110; Nature Conservancy Council pp. 111 below, 103 (E. Hammand), 108 below (D. Harvey), 112 (based on Ordnance Survey Map), 102 (P. Wakeley); Bernard Price pp. 100/101 (Walter Noah Malby); RSPB p. 105 (Dennis Green).

First published 1978 by
MACMILLAN LONDON LTD
London and Basingstoke
Associated companies in Delhi, Dublin,
Hong Kong, Johannesburg, Lagos, Melbourne,
New York, Singapore and Tokyo

Printed in Great Britain by
Butler & Tanner Ltd, Frome and London

British Library Cataloguing in Publication Data

Williamson, Richard
    The Great Yew Forest
    1. Kingley Vale National Nature Reserve
    History
    I. Title
    639'.95'0942262   QH77.G7

    ISBN 0-333-22739-5

Contents

Author's Note

As I am no expert in the several fields which I have tried to cover I hope that the reader with specialised knowledge will not begrudge me the occasional mistake should it occur but will instead give me the benefit of his knowledge.

Readers are reminded that the taking of any specimens, including flowers and insects, is not allowed on this or any nature reserve, unless a permit has been granted for scientific research.

I would like to thank Mike Schofield and David Harvey, Regional and Assistant Regional Officers (South-East Region) of The Nature Conservancy Council for their help and useful criticism of the text. Janet Cragg worked very hard deciphering and typing the manuscript. My special thanks go to my wife Anne for constant encouragement and post-natal care of the work.

Lastly may I pay tribute to those staff behind office doors of The Nature Conservancy Council without whom Kingley Vale National Nature Reserve would not function, and to all my voluntary wardens – in particular Major W. W. A. Phillips, M.B.E., Michael Boxall and Keith Burn who have given up so much of their time in the day-to-day running of the reserve.

R. W.
January 1978

Foreword

England's heritage of beautiful places is under greater pressure than ever before. Numerous official and voluntary organisations and their many reports testify to the conflicts around them and the dramatic changes so visible to those who care for this vital heart of our country.

Fortunately there are glimmers of hope that the nation's mood is moving to demand that the quality of our landscapes and the rich diversity of our wildlife be safeguarded. One great beacon to the way ahead is the monumental work *A Nature Conservation Review*, published in 1977. This describes the most important sites in Britain – of National Nature Reserve status – that should be conserved for our wealth of habitats and wild flora and fauna. Kingley Vale, among the first National Nature Reserves to be established in England, is one of these Grade 1 sites.

Kingley Vale is an area which combines exceptional landscape quality with very high scientific interest. But few nature reserves can be left to themselves. Most owe their existence to man's activities and demand constant attention to maintain their principal features. It is the Nature Conservancy Council's task to ensure that the magnificent yew wood can perpetuate itself by natural regeneration and that the chalk grassland with its characteristic flowers and butterflies is maintained by suitable grazing.

Kingley Vale, as this book reveals, is fortunate in having a dedicated warden whose wide-ranging knowledge, coupled with great practical skills, ensures that it is maintained with understanding. The reserve's fine condition, which is readily apparent to visitors, testifies to the splendid work of its custodian.

R. E. BOOTE
Director
Nature Conservancy Council

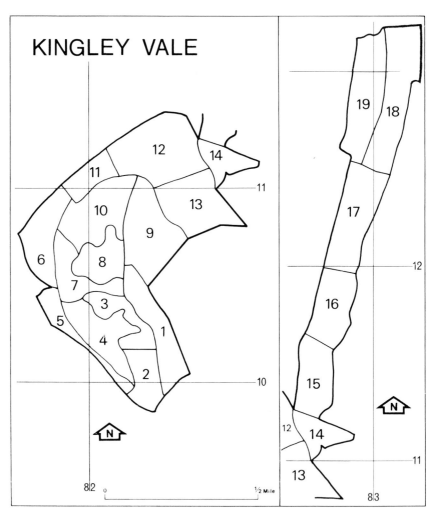

KINGLEY VALE

A map of the reserve divided into compartments, to make easier the task of recording plants and animals.

Introduction to Kingley Vale

Arrival

The motorbike with its royal-blue petrol tank sped out of East Anglia towards the Sussex coast on a warm September morning in 1963. Two years of unsettled no man's land, of unhappy attempts to find temporary jobs in the country to tide me over until this moment arrived, were over. No more selling cultivators to sceptical farmers, no more putting up cow barriers covered in wet paint only to watch the cows licking it off, no more writing idealistic prose which boomeranged back out of editors' offices all over the country. No more by-passing the dole queue, to return home once more with empty pockets but undented pride.

For at last I had got the sort of job I had always wanted. Ever since I had seen the first blackbird's eggs lying like smooth faded lapis lazuli in the nest over the old duck pond on my father's farm in Norfolk, and had seen that same nest with its naked young ones pulled to pieces by village boys and wrecked in front of my eyes, I had resolved deep inside me that my work must lie in helping such defenceless creatures. This resolve meant that much of my life had been spent in gaining the knowledge and experience which would help me, by the time I reached the regulation age of twenty-six, to gain a post as warden in the Nature Conservancy – summer jobs helping wardens along the Norfolk coast, forestry jobs gaining knowledge of management, farming jobs learning about machinery, and above all minute and prolonged observation of wildlife in all its intricate aspects. Wardens' posts were few and far between, and it was not until now at the age of twenty-eight that the envelope bearing 'On Her Majesty's Service' had informed me that there was a post vacant in Sussex. The two difficult years of waiting were over – years of doubts that the planned career as an unusual species of Civil Servant would ever materialise – and I had at last got the job which would allow me to protect and look after and improve a piece of countryside, allow me to study all its animals, birds, insects and plants.

'Kingley Vale National Nature Reserve', the letter said, 'is situated on a chalky outcrop of the South Downs. Within a dry coombe, a yew forest, described as the finest in Europe, covers steep slopes. There are enclaves of old downland turf and on the plateau fragments of chalk heath still exist. Fine views are obtainable over the Sussex Plain and the channel coast.' I had tried to visualise it every moment of the two months up to the day of my appointment. A wild landscape of grassy glades filled with beautiful flowers; deer, badgers and foxes running in the dew; butterflies emerging in the morning as the dew burned away. I had never been to Sussex, but had learned about it in old books by W. H. Hudson and Charles Knox. It was, I knew, the county of winding, dusty, chalk tracks crossing the gentle sloping and rounded hills of the downs, of branch lines running down to seaside villages such as Angmering and Littlehampton, where fishing boats came in with a grinding of gravel on the keel and where there were shrimps and brown bread and butter for tea. Stone curlews and wheatears nested on the old sheep-bitten turf. It was a paradise, and at the thought of it I threaded the motorbike at high speed in and out of the cat's-eyes on the empty road.

Somewhere near Reigate or Redhill – places never even imagined – it began to rain. The motorbike slid on a turning hill, pulled off course by my load of boots and books, and we slithered down into the town. An angry lorry snarled behind. The rain formed white spray as it bounced back off the road. I realised that I was tired and hungry, and having bought a plastic-coated sausage roll as an excuse for sitting in the dry, I spent an hour in a roadside café looking out with apprehension at the jungle beyond the window. I had never seen so much traffic, and it behaved in the same chaotic way as the cars of the Arabs in a Middle Eastern town which I had visited some years previously while in the Air Force. I got out the maps and looked for the South Downs. They stretched benignly, coloured green, across the map. Leaving the cafe (and not sure whether I had taken off enough layers of plastic from the sausage roll to have rendered it edible), I set off into the rain. Occasionally a forlorn tree approached and then passed me. There were small fields with ponies grazing, and some woods that would have seemed empty to a town mind but which I knew were full of occupants. Once I passed a station, and the car-park filled with Jaguars stretched for several acres.

When I came to the foot of the downs I had that awful coldness found only on mountains and motorbikes. The rain had gone through the layers of newspaper stuffed into my shirt, but that didn't mar my first sight of the South Downs near a little village called Duncton. I liked them at once, these rounded, expansive hills with the hint of wilderness still about them. There were no big towns here. The rain filled the air midway towards their many heights like a mountain mist. The hill of Duncton is very steep; the motorbike seemed to need a lower gear than I had ever used before on hills, and I began to think something was wrong. As I went upwards as if on a cable car I watched the bank along the verge, and although I did not know my plants as well as I ought, I knew that it was all different here. Pebbles of chalk had spilled down into the roads, and that reminded me of very long ago when my father had farmed a small, hilly, chalk farm in Norfolk. I knew it for a benign soil, which had lived once already, unlike the sour igneous rock of the north and west. And gradually I realised that some of the plants which I had not seen for a score of years were familiar. I stopped and propped the bike against a fallen beech log. What were these dry, brown stems no longer than my hand, which rattled like tiny babies' rattles when I shook them? And this fine-leaved grass with slender stems and a pale head like a fox's brush? It was the end of the season and not much was still in flower, but slowly they began to click into place in my childhood memory. I remembered totter grass, salad burnet with its cucumber-tasting leaves, and some mauve and pink flowers which someone had said were orchids.

The Nature Conservancy report had promised remnants of just such ancient turf at Kingley Vale, and so once again I set off, with renewed optimism. Over the top of the hill the rain stopped and the sun shone in a long green valley that stretched towards the west. The stubble on the hillsides high on either side of the valley had recently been fired, exposing hundreds of acres of smooth chalk slope which gleamed like snowfields in the sun. There were flint-faced barns and a herd of black and white cows drawing down from the slopes to be milked. The road turned off down a very narrow lane, milky with chalk dust. It was as if it had never rained, although my tyre tracks showed the lane to be freshly overlaid by water. The valley went on and on, with grey flint houses gathered like tumbled moraine drift every mile or so. At one of these I suddenly came out of my reverie and wondered where I was going. Kingley Vale was near Chichester, and so was I, but I did not have a local map. It was time to camp for the night.

Everybody seemed to know of Kingley Vale. 'It's away westerly', they all said, pointing vaguely over a high green hill. 'It's our local beauty spot.' 'Our' was pronounced 'air', when it should have been 'ower' according to the dialect I had been used to. This discovery set me back subconsciously, though I was not aware of it at the time. Kingley Vale belonged, it seemed not to me, nor to the native tongue I knew, but to an alien group of people of different speech. 'Jealously guarded rights of access', the official dossier had warned. 'This reserve is a local beauty spot, where the public have been able to walk and have recreation for centuries.' It was not to be my place at all. It was their place, and they might thank me to mind my own business. Every nook and cranny had already been explored; there would be little chance to stamp my individuality upon it. Time was to heal this first impression, but it was with some trepidation that I set off the next morning on the last five miles to the nature reserve.

It lay north of a hamlet whose Saxon church with its miniature steeple reminded me of a very old photograph in a Richard Jefferies book, in which the village church was called 'the cathedral of the downs'. Grey lichened tombstones were slowly sinking into the graves which they had marked for three hundred years. A grove of beech trees sighed uneasily in that dry, grey September wind which is the wind of change for trees and birds. It was old English parkland, with browse-lines under the horse chestnuts and the beech; a little owl whooped sorrowfully, a blackbird mobbing it somewhere high up in the branches, and a narrow lane led away through old hedgerows in which hawthorns were already ripe. From this a flint-strewn track went northwards into the distance of the downs, seen as no more than a grey-green line.

And so the last stage of my journey to Kingley Vale began on foot – which is a good way to face any encounter, giving one time to prepare oneself, the physical exertion removing any feelings of dread within the pit of the stomach. For a little way the downs hid behind a woodland of tall old beech trees and some oaks and yews. By the field gate was an ivy-covered hawthorn bush, and out of this flew a small black and white bird which sat above me on the beech branches flicking its wings. It was the first pied flycatcher that I had ever seen, a little brighter and smaller than the coloured illustrations in the many bird books that I had owned from the age of six. It had probably been passing through on migration from the Welsh nature reserves. That particular part of the woods came to be called by me 'flycatcher gate', because a spotted flycatcher always nested in the ivy-covered hawthorn tree and often its pied cousin loitered there on migration.

Along this last stretch of the track to the reserve, I noted several unusual shrubs that I had never seen before, some with umbels of clustered black berries and with wine-coloured leaves. Bines of clematis festooned the branches, and among them stood a yew tree actually inside the field, its trunk covered with a bristle of hard, thin leaves which had been browsed by the cattle. There was something curious in its

SPOTTED
FLYCATCHER

upper twigs: small, waxy red drops stuck to the branches and twigs, like the carmine ends of old vestas matches. A mistle thrush chackled and looped away in a swinging flight towards the north, to disappear into a wild and rich old woodland wherein many different trees and shrubs were scattered in clumps among rough grassland. The woodland seemed to cover half a mile of gently rising valley; in the distance it rose steeply to a high downland ridge. This was Kingley Vale.

As I walked into the valley along a dusty track marked here and there by horses' hoofprints, I was excited by the realisation that this was wilderness. I had seen it only once or twice before in this country, and once abroad in the Black Desert of Syria; it was instantly recognisable by the great variety of wildlife which, though not familiar, nevertheless gladdened the embittered eye of the naturalist used to seeing destruction, pollution and a continual and expected diminution of variety. I had to stop almost at once, for example, to watch a procession of clouded yellow butterflies on their journey to the south. These were almost unseen in my home county. Small beetles, shiny in emerald and azure, crawled secretly among the deep grass and foliage. Orb web spiders, heavy with feeding on sweat flies, hung in their webs that stretched a foot or so wide and were slung by twisted hawsers to the twigs around them. Everything was rich and full with the sweetness of autumn.

I wandered on, into the valley and its woodlands encircling the path. At first the valley slopes on either side rose gently and were wide apart; ahead I could see that they narrowed and ended abruptly in a very steep hill. These slopes were covered with a dense yew forest, crown upon crown touching and leaving no opening, a canopy of dark green. Thus they formed an amphitheatre, and in the pit of this I felt small – not insignificant, but rather, out of place. The human shape intruded within this natural landscape, as it would not in any man-made countryside. Deeper into the wood I went, and came upon some ancient trees whose boughs drooped around them and touched the ground. These yews, when I had penetrated one of the few cleft entrances under their hanging crowns, were of weird shapes. The trunks were ruddy brown, smooth, but twisted and bulging with a dozen secret recesses where wrens could nest and squirrels hide themselves. I could only guess the girth, but thought that it might be well over twenty feet. One monster had grown such a long bough that this had broken near the trunk and now hung down with a splintered gape like a crocodile's mouth.

These were no carefully kept and propped-up churchyard yews with

14

concreted cavities – they were wild and hoary with age, they saw the passing of deer and fox and had weathered a thousand winters. From the crowns, drooping bines of clematis hung down to the ground like liana stems, thick as ships' ropes, forming an enclosed, dry place like the inside of a church. On this humid autumn day, it was cool. It would be a wonderful place in the height of summer. The ground was bare – no grass, no plants of any kind. Perhaps this was due to the lack of light? Around the roots I could see, when my eyes were used to the gloom, those red waxy blobs that had been growing on the twigs. I had no idea what kind of fruit the yew tree bore, and had imagined a small fir cone. But here it was, a red, soft cup, fleshy and smooth, not much larger than a pea. The berries hung on the twigs above, like Chinese lanterns; they looked good to eat.

Standing still and looking around I noticed a mistle thrush feasting on the waxy berries, and then another and another, everywhere I looked. They were not all mistle thrushes either – some were the smaller cousins, song thrushes. They slipped in and out of sight as they moved from twig to twig. The whole forest was moving with thrushes, and I became aware of a subdued, almost whispering sound, which was the myriads of song thrushes quietly singing to themselves. This was the subsong that I had heard individual birds singing in the autumn hedges at home. I had never heard a choir of birds performing. The soft whistles merged from all sides of the enclosed valley as though I were, again, within a vast building, but one with a roof open to the sky. For there, above all the song, the birds, the wild flowers and clusters of dark trees, was the autumn sky going from blue to a smoky gold – early afternoon yet, and a more dusky colour than I was used to in the clean open skies of the east. Already part of the valley was in shade, its western side where a grove of ash trees grew among the yew forest, stretching up for five hundred feet to the hill. I had a great deal more to explore before the day was out, and it was already well past midday.

I was not sure where the reserve boundaries were, since the wild downland in places merged with forestry and rough grazing. The way seemed to lead north again, out of the grove towards the hill, through a sloping meadow where another forest edge advanced. The old turf was strewn with green mounds, each over a foot across. What could they be? Each one grew its own particular crop of flowers, like a miniature rock garden, and each was different from the last. I had no idea what all the flowers could be, especially as many of them were now over. The rosette leaves were mostly unfamiliar. But, as on the roadside verge during my journey up Duncton Hill, there were enough of the familiar childhood flowers such as totter grass to give me hope of one day identifying them all. This rock garden stretched for twenty or thirty acres, and enclaves almost hidden behind outcrops of yew trees showed that it extended even further. Tall coarse grass, rather like a wild oat, crept over much of the area.

I wandered on, climbing the hill and passing through an extensive yew forest, where the ground was bare and lower branches entangled each other as though the whole forest was matted and clasping itself against the intruder. Deer tracks and droppings were scattered here and there. There were owl pellets under a tree, and small whispering birds flew quietly away from above. The sun had gone. This was the 'sinister and fantastic' forest that had inspired Victorian writers, and I was relieved when I broke out of its shrouding darkness on to the hill. It was to be a year or two before I came to terms with that enclosing canopy of trees that stretched for nearly a mile. Meanwhile, in the coming winter particularly, I was to find that in several small and subtle ways its character was not always benign; it did not yield easily to a mind used to birds and open skies, the more obvious side of nature. It would be no exaggeration to say that at times it was hostile.

Settling Down

My brief in the first week was to define the boundaries of the reserve. At its southern end, which is the natural entrance to the valley, the reserve appeared to be an island within the agricultural scene. Scrub and trees, grass and herbs sprouted at the very teeth of the cultivators now ripping open the brown earth in the surrounding fields. This contrast gave the reserve a very neat appearance, like a flower bed set off by a well-kept lawn. The eye enjoyed the sudden vertical structure of leaf colours, opposed to the horizontal stripes of brown plough line. But further northwards up the hill the island became a peninsula, joined to the most wild and tangled thickets of thorn and yew, bramble and beech. Here the boundaries had all but vanished. Since they partly followed the parish boundary of West Dean and Binderton it seemed sensible to seek the kind of line that parish boundary-markers of previous centuries would have looked for.

Starting on the east, I looked for natural features through the overgrown downland meadow. There was a deep sunken trackway running north, near to the boundary, and recent rain had worked considerable fans of chalk rubble into the field from the bed of this track.

Over the centuries thousands of tons of chalk must have been worn away since the first sledges had scored the hillside on their way over the steep shoulder. What a mighty pull it must have been then for the oxen, and how the horses would have struggled there in the past four hundred years. Their many thousand hooves had pounded the bedrock to powder, and now all that had gone.

The banks of this trackway were now, in some places, fifteen to twenty feet below the level of the downland. The slopes were a tiny scree of chalk pea-shingle, heated and cracked into dry particles by years of direct sun. Very little grew there, but I imagined there would be orchids among the 'pioneer' tufts of plants such as bird's-foot trefoil and salad burnet. The boundary, however, was not on this obvious landmark. According to maps it was twenty yards to the east, and I wondered why until, running downslope, I tripped in an old rabbit burrow, fell forward and rolled under the low branches of a yew. My glissade continued unexpectedly for several more yards until I was in a dark cavern beneath the tree, completely hidden from outside. This was yet another sunken track, as steep as the last, running parallel but now no longer used. It was an obvious parish boundary. This track wound northwards, and I followed it like a badger following a tunnel: it burrowed through the undergrowth, revealing every thirty yards an old rotten post set there by some forgotten surveyor when the reserve was first acquired. I began to realise that my boyhood training as a country wanderer, bird-nester and 'general oddmedod', as a master at school had described me, was now coming into its own. The ability to crawl and worm one's way under bramble bushes appeared to be essential for a warden's job.

So I continued, in a great horseshoe, until dusk fell and all of the northern boundary was rediscovered. It seemed that my first job was to hack my way through these 'tangly woods' so that my departmental boss, more used to the tangled political corridors of an embryo civil service department, could see the boundary for himself. As I hacked my way through the clematis bines and the brambles throughout the autumn, a more exciting fact emerged than scrub clearance. It was that I was not alone in this task. Thousands upon thousands of people had worked, hunted and even lived up on this hill and in the valley below. Daily, the evidence of past human agriculture and settlement became evident; it began with my 'discovery' of the sunken trackway, and immediately after this I found artefacts. Potboilers were very common. These are flints deeply honeycombed with hairline fractures, which gives them a greyish appearance. They were used by Stone Age man for heating and even boiling water, by being first heated in hot embers and then carefully lowered into an urn of water, this being repeated until the water boiled. (Stone Age man did not, of course, have fireproof utensils.) There was abundant evidence of his agricultural occupation as far back as the late Bronze Age at least. Nearly the whole of the valley floor was cultivated in the years up to the Middle Ages. An ancient system of small fields shown by lynchets and smaller traces of banks could be identified on the tongue of higher ground between the two lesser valleys to east and west. Unfortunately the better example of this mosaic of fields, in the eastern half, had been partly obliterated by more recent cultivation in the Second World War. All the evidence pointed to a period of settled and probably peaceful occupation. With the south-facing valley acting as a sun trap and permanently sheltered from north and east winds, a long run of crops could have been grown each year, provided the rainfall was constant in the summer. The field banks were set out in squares usually running on prime compass boundaries, though this might have been accidental.

The most noble monuments left behind by the Bronze Age men were the four tumuli on the summit of Bow Hill. Two of these could be seen for many miles: the inhabitants of the coastal plain, in Bognor Regis and Chichester, would look north as the sun was setting and see the mounds, clear and far away. They were skyline monuments. Local people called them the Devil's Humps. Only night, or fog, or the Valhalla rain-curtain could hide them from the people below. The story went that the devil could be evoked by running around them backwards, at the same time reciting the Lord's Prayer backwards. They were built in two pairs, each pair being identical. Those most clearly visible were bell barrows, whose outlines suggested the flowing lower terrace or beam of a church bell. The two to the north-east, almost hidden by trees and scrub, were bowl barrows, being pure pudding shape: perhaps a blancmange that had collapsed and was on the move across the plate. All four had been plundered – the records told of a sudden interest in antiquities in the eighteenth century. The tumuli had originally been tombs, with small chambers in which the cremation urns were placed. One local Victorian farmer had dug energetically into twenty or thirty local barrows and tumuli, recovering earthenware cremation pots which he gave to his friends' wives for flower pots. All had been lost, save the remains of one which is still in Lewes Museum. So the centres were hollowed out, and even on very windy days, when it was bitterly cold elsewhere on that open plateau, it was possible to sit cupped in the palm of the centre, out of the wind. Many a summer dawn I was to lie therein, watching the reddening sky over the Iron Age fort on Goodwood hill. How very remote those dawns of man's occupation of the valley seemed, yet I was constantly aware of the ancestors who had worked and fought, built and destroyed there, thousands of years before. Often I felt that they were watching me.

I was most interested to see a tumulus which had been uncovered in Kent, at about this time. This tumulus had been used in the years after its construction as a communal burial ground. After the top six inches of soil had been carefully removed, as though one had peeled the top half of an orange, half-a-dozen skeletons had been exposed in shallow graves; plough shares searing over the compacted chalk after the introduction of the iron plough had missed them by millimetres. But the Devil's Humps of this reserve remain an enigma to this day – though an excavation of one of them in 1936 revealed one or two oddments such as a horse's tooth, a bone awl and some shards of pottery. How I would like to have seen these barrows in their original state. Then they would have gleamed white in the sun on the pinnacle of the downs, or glowed with a soft luminosity as chalk does on summer nights, reminding the people in the valleys of their late king, and of their allegiance to his successors.

The view from these tumuli stretches to the north, as well as to the south. From the north came a grey wind that blew all winter, a cold, dry air that was as piercing here as it was in Norfolk; it somehow made that north view for me for evermore, giving a hint of wilderness to the far ridge of south downland that runs from Cocking through Bepton and Didling, Treyford and Telegraph Hill to Marden Forest, and over the hill to Harting. Up Park House, staring across the intervening three miles of valley, is Wellington's house still, offered to him after Waterloo but turned down on account of its inaccessibility for his horses. To me it seems a ghost house, inhabiting a wild landscape untamed despite its legions of beech plantation and fields. You could see nobody, there was little hint even of people out there, and the far ridge ended in the grey cold air that had come from the east coast.

Close by in the valley under Bow Hill is the village of Stoughton – and what a perfect village it is, proportioned as no other I have seen, save perhaps the late eighteenth-century mellowed brick villages of north Norfolk. Stoughton was then, and still is if you look only at its centre, a settlement of downland flint, not scattered but compact, and resembling the battlements of a great castle three-quarters submerged in green. As the seasons came and went, over the years I noticed curious circles and lines developing like photographs a mile below in the Stoughton valley, showing the settlements and encampments, fields and tumuli of ancient days, fading away for a season or a couple of years until conditions were right again.

When the Ancient Britons felt insecure they retreated to the tops of hills such as Bow Hill and barricaded themselves in. Earth walls with sharpened palings to face the enemy were erected in a grand circle, as at Old Winchester Hill, the Trundle at Goodwood and many others. These were the Iron Age forts, and visiting these green peaceful mounds today one may find it difficult to imagine the turmoil of milling cattle and horses, dogs, frightened children, women huddled cooking at open fires and men waiting with spears and bows on the top of the walls. The enclosure at Bow Hill is even less easy to imagine, as only one wall is visible and that is the western wall. It descends either side of the hill, half-forgotten in the trees, and on its southern descent it fades clean away among the loose scree under the yews. The other three ramparts are hidden.

There is hardly an acre of the reserve that does not show the past activity of man, including not only the prehistoric monuments but more recent activities, such as the slit trenches, the dug-outs and the guerilla hide-out under the oldest yews. Over the weeks of 'boundary bashing' I came across many more strange mounds and hollows. At the far northern end of the steep escarpment slope facing east was an area of land not then in the reserve, and completely hidden within an almost inaccessible series of glades among the yews, called Goosehill Camp. It is marked on the maps as two banked circles that cover two or three acres. Apart from round 'banjo' enclosures in other parts of the south there are few prehistoric engineering works quite like this. Is it so old, or is it Saxon? What is the origin of the name, which has not altered over the period of the maps deposited in the County archives, a period of a mere 400–500 years?

But what of recent history? No one walking even casually could help seeing the terrible damage to the trees during the last war. The ground too is deeply scarred and pocked with craters, tank tracks, diggings and dug-outs, showing a far from peaceful occupation of more recent times. Stories of the war emerged slowly but were scant. After all it was twenty years ago! I met my neighbour Fred Longman, bailiff of the 700-acre downland farm adjoining our eastern boundary. Fred had started in 1918 as a shepherd boy, and his flocks had cropped the turf short not just on Kingley Vale but across much of the land now growing barley every year. 'Italian prisoners cleared away all the yew trees. We had fifty of them working out here and one time we had fifty land girls too. In the war Canadians took over the Vale. They were a bad lot. You had to be careful if you were working out on the fields. They'd fire at you!' His face still showed the surprise he had felt twenty years previously as 303 bullets spun and ricocheted off the familiar flints he had known since boyhood. 'One day the Sergeant asked for a horse and cart. They'd had a battle in the yew trees. There were several dead. I had to bring them out and take them down to the mortuary.' Bullets had splashed like sparks in a foundry. Ash trees showed their wounds as sequences of glancing grooves, climbing up the smooth grey trunks. Yews did not heal. The wounds festered with, at best, minute pink or white fungus, at worst honey tuft which attacked tissue and the core. Several copper-green bullets still stuck where they had hit a quarter of a century before. One group of trees running up the centre of the valley stood like skeletons where they had been killed by ricochets. The target had stood directly below them. Now clematis tried to clothe them. I was surprised to discover from old photographs that many large yews had once grown on the slopes near the skeletons, but now all that remained were circles of dogwood shrubs.

'That was our Army', said Fred. 'They had to see how many mortar bombs they could use to knock the yews over. They'd go on all day and half the night if there was a moon – sometimes when there weren't no moon', he added as an afterthought. Tanks had ground their way up the flanks, digging twin furrows of chalk where now the bee orchid and the frog orchid grow – the fresh chalk being much favoured by these strange plants. One day, when the war was over, someone noticed in the centre of the valley (a place like a small glen) a rusty tomb of metal which had been a Centurion tank. There had been letters before to *The Times* about the Army's despoliation of Kingley Vale, urging that it should be, before too long, released. Could not the tank be removed? Its absence would be its best memorial to an unhappy time. The Army agreed, and arrived to destroy it with dynamite. The historian Bernard Price was there at the time:

They laid a charge under it and told everyone within half a mile to keep back. There was much interest because of course as youngsters we had all been in the Vale during operations and had known the tank well. We used to picnic on it. At the appointed time we heard a dull roar. Someone who was watching saw the tank lift one foot off the ground and settle back exactly as it had been before. Of course we all laughed and fell about. They said they'd be back in a week. We came again and stood ready for another laugh. There was an incredible bang and a shoot of dark red flame. We heard bits going everywhere, some landed on top of the hill. The prize pieces were ball bearings, as big as pigeon eggs. The tank had vanished and there was a little saucer shape in the chalk like a small dew pond.

So the slings and arrows continued to dominate the fortunes of this historic, bloody-battled valley, until a truce was called in the middle of this century. In 1949 the Nature Conservancy, a newly constituted government agency, was empowered to establish and maintain nature reserves to provide areas 'for the study of, and research into, matters relating to the fauna and flora of Great Britain' and for the purpose of 'preserving flora, fauna or geological or physiographical features of special interest' (*National Parks and Access to the Countryside Act*, 1949). And so the official ball of nature conservation started rolling.

The first Chairman of the Nature Conservancy was Sir Arthur Tansley, who had a special affection for the South Downs, and from his Whitehall office remembered Kingley Vale. He remembered too the remark of a German colleague, one Professor Drude, who visited the Vale in 1911 and became very enthusiastic, exclaiming 'You did not tell me you were going to show me the finest yew forest in Europe!'

Tansley saw to it that Kingley Vale was acquired for the nation in 1952, two halves of the valley being purchased separately from two local farmers. He lived only three more years, and in 1957 his memorial stone was erected at almost the exact spot where he had so often enjoyed the view. A Sarsen stone was chosen from the Totterdown area, part of Fyfield Down National Nature Reserve in Wiltshire; it was brought on a lorry and laid on 2 November 1957. A bronze plaque fixed to the stone had this inscription:

> *In the midst of this nature reserve*
> *which he brought into being this*
> *stone calls to memory Sir Arthur*
> *George Tansley, F.R.S., who during*
> *a long lifetime strove with success*
> *to widen the knowledge, to deepen the*
> *love, and to safeguard the heritage·*
> *of nature in the British Isles.*

With the boundaries marked out and at least an inkling of what the reserve was all about, I began to study the Management Plan written in 1959 by scientific members of the Nature Conservancy staff. Reserve management plans, by which all reserves work, ensure continuity of purpose whoever is in charge and are agreed by a scientific committee of different disciplines. It had been impressed upon me in the first place that before one could manage a reserve, one must understand at least the most essential ingredients of its 'interest'. Secondly, 'management' was almost always likely to be necessary to maintain a particular habitat, since it had only got to its present state through some quirk of economic pressure. What would this management mean to me, a layman still? It was all very specialised and I began to be aware of my own inadequacies. I knew that Kingley Vale consisted of three essential ingredients, chalk grassland, scrub and yew forest. What to do with them all? How to manage them, what to keep out and what to keep in?

The first easily grasped fact was that chalk grassland needed to be grazed if the dozens of miniature plants were not to be stifled by scrub or taller grass. This had once been done by rabbits, but they had been wiped out by the myxomatosis plague of 1953. Sheep seemed to be an alternative grazing animal if a farmer could be persuaded to keep them there. Meanwhile, the turf was, year by year, losing square yards, even acres of its character and becoming overgrown by scrub. Right – the first thing to do was to get grazing animals installed, and to cut out the scrub with billhook, saw or winch.

But the solution was not to be as simple as that. The first snag presented itself one early summer day in May when I walked in the 'blossom garden', as I have always called it ever since, at the extreme south-western edge of the reserve, where young shrubs – one could no longer call it scrub – were in flower. Snowy clusters of flowers on hawthorn, dogwood, wayfaring tree and whitebeam dazzled the eye, and a mixture of sweet and pungent scents flowed as thick as mist. Insects – flies, butterflies, beetles and solitary wasps – floundered in the sea of sweetness that flowed for them like milk and honey. Brimstone butterflies visited and imbibed from the buckthorn bush, and laid their eggs singly on leaves behind the tiny green flowers. Surely the scrub was a very rich habitat in its own right?

Snag number two arose when I read the studies carried out by Dr A. S. Watt on the origin of yew sites in 1926. Dr Watt had made a particular study of the yew forests of the South Downs. It was after all a particularly, if locally, common tree, known in Hampshire as 'the Hampshire weed', and with its pagan connections was surely as interesting as the oak. But because of its low commercial value, except to the specialists, it had excited little economic planning – unlike the oak. Watt had discovered that scrub played an important part in the life of the yew tree. Seeds might be dropped into all kinds of unlikely places by birds, and after eighteen months they would sprout, but unless they were in exactly the right place they would not live. They needed moisture, shade, shelter, freedom from aerial competitors (but not presumably from root competitors), freedom from browsing animals such as rabbits, sheep and deer, and a chalky soil. (Possibly they thrived on chalky soil because other trees could not, so there was no competition.) The provender of nearly all its requirements was scrub.

Scrub held moisture in the topsoil which otherwise would rapidly transpire on the surface of steep slopes facing the sun. Nurserymen had discovered how seedling yews needed slats of wood criss-crossed over them in summer if they were to survive hot sun, so the necessary shade for the delicate leaves was provided by the lattice-work of scrub twigs. According to Watt, the type of scrub at Kingley Vale was one of three, depending on exposure to the prevailing winds. Juniper was common on the most exposed sites facing the south-west wind. Hawthorn on the next most exposed slopes, followed by hawthorn and ash, protected from the south-west winds, were the other scrub nurseries. Under these spiny cages the yew seedling was safe from most animals. The yew soon outgrew its nurse and suppressed it, despite frantic efforts by many junipers, blackthorns and hawthorns to keep their heads above the closing green sea of foliage deepening and closing all around them. At Kingley Vale in the dark greeny-black caverns of underwood were many dead junipers lying in perfect state of preservation, dry and polished by the climbing claws of mouse, like a fossilised and forgotten wood. Most of them had never had a chance when their precocious foster-children, one year under their skirts, the next at their shoulder, the next trying to hold hands over the heads of their nursemaids, had started to grow. The juniper skeletons were of the round, short, well-branched structure which they had developed against the attacks of what they thought were their only enemies, the sheep, the deer and the wind; but in the event death had come from within the ranks.

Dead juniper can be distinguished from any other kind of shrub by the simple experiment of breaking open a twig. It gives off a sweet smell of lead pencils – in other words, the smell of cedar wood, as it is of course in the same family. Living junipers there were few and far between. I have made those few bushes, about a hundred in number, the subject of a special study. Once a common shrub, juniper is now declining rapidly throughout Britain, so it is dear to conservationists. Its decline is possibly due to climatic factors, to a virus which debilitates the new shoots, and to cattle grazing across the few remaining large stands where it still exists. It is not, in short, 'scrub'.

If hawthorn was equally important in the establishment of the forest, why should it be cleared? Looking around with Watt's words and diagrams fresh in my mind I soon found the perfectly proportioned little yew trees hiding delicately, untouched by drought, browsing or competition from more lofty competitors such as oak or beech, under the protection of the enveloping hawthorn bush. The blossom garden had its kindergarten, as did the mixed ash and hawthorn up on the western flank and, most impressive of all, the tangled thorn colony on the plateau clay, the crown of Kingley Vale. Here, worming in on my hands and knees (a spine going right into my knee and dealing a wound like a miniature bullet-hole, blue around the edge) I found not a kindergarten, but a complete infant town – hundreds of yew seedlings, most no more than a few inches high, starting another thick forest under the fairly aged hawthorns. These too I was to make the subject of a special study, because a most curious situation developed as the years went by: the yew trees never seemed to grow!

Thus, scrub is important on this particular reserve because it acts as a nurse to the yew seedling. Watt's work had been fully annotated and formed the background to the Kingley Vale Management Plan, which had recognised the part played by the bushes in the welfare of the yews, but due to financial stringencies, and the lack of a full-time warden, active management had so far been minimal, and for all practical purposes the reserve had been under a system of *laissez faire*. The delicate question now was where to cut away the scrub to preserve the downland turf and its unique flora, and where to leave the scrub so that it could form the basis of a future yew forest? In my bedsitter in the city I coloured in a large map, pinned to the wall, with three colours: green for yew trees, brown for scrub, yellow for turf. The mosaic of colours of this half-square-mile of British countryside dominated my existence for months. I even dreamt about it, the colours mixing and swimming round in the dark.

However, it was not long before the Management Plan was revised by the Regional Officer at that time, Dr P. A. Gay. This incorporated Watt's annotated work and the original plan of 1959, and it is by this 1965 version that the reserve is run today. The main objectives of the Management Plan are:

i) to maintain good representative areas of the various yew communities;

ii) to maintain areas of other communities (e.g. chalk grassland, chalk heath, and areas that might lead to development of yew communities);

iii) to preserve the relics of the ancient field systems and other archaeological structures.

To carry out and achieve these apparently simple objectives is a complex business. The Management Plan itself is a document of some 73 pages.

In order to help with the implementation of the Management Plan the reserve was divided into compartments. Clearly defined boundaries are essential in this exercise – boundaries which are easily found, long-lasting, and which if possible put major habitats into one compartment or series of compartments, since this makes management recording and species recording simpler and more workable. Established yew forests have clearly defined boundaries, so these can be used in some cases; a division between yew and yew–ash, or young and middle-aged yews, has to be a theoretical, or compass-bearing line. Scrub and grassland needs some other physical feature – old earth banks, settled trackways or centre lines of gullies are used, or compass bearings on to fixed monuments such as the Tansley Stone.

The reserve at this time was divided into 13 compartments covering 213 acres; after 1968 the new acquisition (along Bow Hill) gave us 19 compartments covering 351 acres, and a further 10 acres were added in 1977. The map on p. 8 shows the compartments.

The Yew Forest

Seeds and Seedlings

The main interest of the reserve lies in its yew forest, which consists of mature, semi-mature and, in a few cases, derelict stages. I knew I had to master its botanical history; I had hardly seen a yew tree in Norfolk, so with the coming of autumn I watched with curiosity the female trees. This in itself was a revelation. There were separate male and female trees. The word, uttered casually by a visiting botanist, to describe this phenomenon was *dioecious*. It was some time before I was able to make sense of the word, not knowing its derivation. The Oxford Dictionary eventually yielded 'having the male and female flowers on separate plants'. It originated from the Greek *oikos*, meaning housed or distinct.

By mid-November the trees were scarlet with berries, hanging like Chinese lanterns. There was a great concourse of thrushes and blackbirds, joined by fieldfares and redwings, which came on the wings of a grey east wind. This wind seemed to arise from the bare chalk fields, drying the ground and spreading a fine powder like muslin over the wood. It brought with it the spirit of winter, which I had known only before on the East Anglian marshes with their wild duck and wild swans. It became very cold. But in the valley we were safe, the flocks of small birds and I. Hardly another human ventured that way all winter, but I had plenty of company. As I cut and hacked my way onwards through scrub I began to observe the birds. This technique of looking objectively at nature has to be learned; at one time, nature had given me an impression only, nearly always one of delight. Then, that had seemed enough – though, as I had discovered with some secret alarm, the force of joy experienced with that first blackbird's nest over the pond during the war had never been repeated, and I was hardly able to admit that my joy had been on an almost imperceptible downward slope ever since.

The fieldfare which sat in the yew tree gobbling berries looked most handsome in his greys, blues, slates, with his speckles, stripes, yellow flashes and other combinations of colours which changed as he moved this way and that, flapping for balance among the green needles. I

27

counted the berries as they disappeared into the bird's yellow throat. Fifteen, twenty, twenty-five – the crop was bulging. Now and then the fieldfare stopped and twisted its neck stiffly to left and right, like a wryneck doing its throat display. It stopped eating and sat looking uncomfortable. Not for long. The load had settled a bit. It struck half-heartedly at another berry by its side: twenty-six. The next two were managed with difficulty. Then suddenly it seemed to have second wind, or an attack of sheer greed. Five more berries vanished in as many seconds. It was too much. The bird flew straight down to the ground, opened its beak and ejected a great stream of pulp and pips. It looked at me, turned and flew straight back into the feast, eating ravenously to fill the great hole it had created. To my astonishment another twenty berries went down before it flew away. The pile of pips on the turf numbered thirty. They had only been lightly bruised or crushed.

Through my binoculars the ground was moving with birds: hundreds of thrushes of various nationalities were availing themselves of the soft turf on which to ease themselves. Fieldfares from Latvia, redwings from Norway, blackbirds from Sweden, song thrushes (a flock of at least one hundred) from England, Belgium, Germany – who knew the origins? The great autumn flood had come on the grey east wind, swept over the east-coast marshes and straight down into the coombes of the south country. Like children confronted by bowls of trifle and jelly, they set to work.

I too set to work to record what was happening. I decided to make a transect along the main turf path leading north, counting all the berries that were spread on this 8-foot wide strip of ground which ran for 250 yards up into the beginning of the yew wood, and so make a record of what kind of seed-spreading ability the bird has, as I was sure nobody would believe a description. Each pile of seed was thrown to one side after having been counted. The operation lasted until the end of November and even into early December. Each day when I arrived there I would make straight for the centre path to see what the twenty-four hours had yielded. These were the yields, month by month: September, 84 pips in 20 separate casts; October, 168; November, 2015; December, 206 – a total of 2473. (The area monitored was nearly one-sixth of an acre.)

Since the valley grassland alone covered some 30 acres it is tempting to assume that nearly half a million berries were scattered every year, at least since records began, when Hudson walked here. What happened to them all? Some of the casts were enormous – 102 berries, 137, 180, and one pile that looked like a small red haggis which topped 200. These were not the work of any bird, and I was intrigued to know what kind of creature could eat 2 lb of yew berries at a meal. My own yellow labrador, Drake, would occasionally pick them up, as he would often pick blackberries off the bush, being very careful not to prick his lips. Eventually I surprised a fox delicately licking the berries off the ground. She stopped with a berry in her mouth when she winded me, lips drawn back baring front teeth. She exactly reminded me of my dog. Another time I came upon a badger in the moonlight smacking his lips as he crunched up berries by the dozen. One day, Fred Longman told me the local name for them. 'Snottygobs, or snot-berries. That's what we used to call them when we were boys. We used to eat them, 'cause we never had so many sweets like youngsters do now. I haven't ate one for years.' Why the name, I wondered. Sticky gluten, spread all over a child's face: not a child, an urchin. The young of pre-technological man would have known how to eat wild fruit, plastering it in with both fists. In all my years at Kingley Vale, I have never seen a child eat them.

To determine the total berry production of the reserve, I needed to estimate the numbers of female trees. A casual glance estimated that the male–female ratio of the number of trees was fifty–fifty. But research revealed the truth. The only way to tackle this was to count trees along the wood edges. Four transect lines were used in widely scattered areas of the reserve, and these were the results of counting, when the yew berry crop was hanging on the twigs, and as a double check, when the male cones were hanging in February:

Transect	Male	Female
1 (plateau)	69	53
2 (plateau)	45	43
3 (slope on west)	139	105
4 (valley)	33	21

The conclusion seemed to be that there was no shortage of yew berries, that the total crop was enormous, and that even taking into account the predation by mice and others there was an adequate germination rate which would be sufficient to recolonise gaps in the woodland over the years. But the gaps were not seeing any permanent regeneration. The next task was to discover why.

Seeds were put out in a number of different areas. Where mice were prevalent, they were eaten within a week. But in an area where there were no mice and 71 per cent of the seeds remained in situ, not one germinated and eighteen months later there were no seedlings. In one plot situated under a mature female tree on the steep slope, the seeds did germinate but none survived. The shade canopy was too dense.

Six hundred seeds were planted out in mouse-proof cages made of small-gauge wire netting. In this secure environment I expected a very high rate of germination, but it was only about 2 per cent, and these soon died off. One hundred seeds were put into a sterilised mixture of sand and peat; only four of these germinated, the others being either empty or attacked by fungi.

This was all very baffling and frustrating and it was not until I came across the work of an American nurseryman, C. E. Heit, that I began to understand the criteria for successful germination, at least in the nursery. Heit had discovered that the seed has to be subjected to particular combinations of cold and warm periods as may in optimum conditions be experienced in the wild. Frost is necessary to break down the seed case and to overcome the 'inherited dormant nature of the embryo and endosperm', for only then can the seed take advantage of spring warmth and sprout. Even then it may take up to three years to germinate. Heit found that with his special treatment he achieved 95 per cent germination success within a three-year period. But controlled nursery experiments are very different from the natural environment. Obviously the Kingley Vale seeds have many problems to overcome within three years, not the least of them being predators.

One of the questions concerning germination is whether the seeds need to be passed through the gut of a bird or animal. My own experiments were inconclusive but Heit found, not that the bird's digestive juices helped in germination as has been suggested, but that a clean seed is more likely to germinate than a pulp-covered one.

There were some areas of the reserve, mainly on the flat, either valley or plateau, where some good regeneration was taking place in patches, mainly under oaks or other deciduous trees. But on the steep slopes and particularly in the gaps, hardly any regeneration was to be found. I began another series of tests and collected some well-established seedlings from outside the reserve and planted them into roughly the same habitats as I had placed the seeds. They all 'took' and were green and healthy-looking by the autumn after being planted in February 1964. From then onwards there were marked differences in their fortunes depending on where they had been planted. Some habitats were clearly unsuitable and although the seedlings lived they looked unhealthy, did not grow and eventually died. The reasons for the non-regeneration of this woodland may be a combination of micro-climate, soil (particularly soil erosion; the ground being bare there is enormous erosion by scree rubble taking away the topsoil), mice, rabbits, hares as well as the more obvious deer.

But there were some areas in which the seedlings did flourish. I was particularly interested in the regeneration of yew which in the 1960s was taking place under old hawthorn on the plateau cap. Scores of yews were sprouting up through the pale buff drifts of those leaves that carpeted the woodland floor in summer and winter. No grass or herbs grew beneath them, but a few brambles here and there and the occasional elderberry accompanied the well-stocked yew 'shrub layer' or field layer, as it almost was.

When I first saw the yews they seemed to be about ten years old, which would tie up nicely with the onset of myxomatosis in 1954. Each year the yew bushes were there, just exactly as they had been the year before, no higher, no fewer, no more. After a few years I marked some, and then it dawned on me what was happening. They were not in fact the same bushes at all. There was a constant coming and going, mainly going. The gradual increase of deer, coinciding with an increase in hares in the early 1970s, accelerated the effect of browsing which had limited the height and the existence of some of the bushes. And so I fixed rabbit-wire cages around half of each lot in the sample glades, and sat back to watch them shoot skywards.

Regeneration of yews was also occurring on the western slopes in tall grassland dominated by upright brome grass, which had lately been short turf. Mainly on the perimeter of female trees – especially those standing alone – but also out in the open, in company with ash, whitebeam, hawthorn, buckthorn, the yews were clearly not going to form any dense canopy: rather were they in the position of pioneers. Presumably this was the case a hundred years ago lower down the western slope below the present-day regeneration. Here widely scattered old yews of about 180–200 years of age with well-branched crowns, looking more like oaks with their leaves shed, had emerged alone, probably when a grazing relaxation had allowed the juniper to develop as well. Long afterwards, yew 'families' had emerged, these being conspicuous by their long slender trunks. The 'families' are clearly seen – an average of four trees grown from under one juniper bush, each family quite distinct from its neighbours which may be twenty yards away. The family may consist of one fat member, average girth 5 feet, two medium-sized, 3 feet, and one skinny member with as little as 2 inches girth. That they are all a hundred years of age was hardly believable, until I counted the annual rings of a score of such families which had been cut down on neighbouring land adjoining cattle pasture.

It was a little tricky to predict exactly how this embryo woodland would develop, on the western slope, but the guess was that it would go at first pretty much like that on the plateau just described, where even-aged thorns and scattered yews grow. The thorns being at the end of their lives, and the older yews only a third of the way or less, with many up and coming youngsters to replace them, presumably an almost full yew canopy was to emerge. That is, before the deer arrived. The deer, it seems, are not even to allow the first stage or 'pioneer' woodland to develop just yet on the western slope. They have so severely stunted bushes under the 4-foot high browse-line that the effect is a set of dwarf shrubs conical in shape, as though unskilled topiary work had been practised upon them. Meanwhile the rest of the shrubs mentioned, with the exception of ash, are able to get ahead. The yews would eventually be able to compete with this deciduous scrub if at any time deer browsing pressure were relaxed.

Distribution of the Yew

The yew (*Taxus baccata L.*) is found wild in most countries of Europe, extending from Scandinavia and Estonia as far as North Africa and eastwards to the Crimea and Western Himalayas where it ascends to 11,000 feet. In Britain it occurs from Perth and Argyll southwards, and in Ireland is found mainly in the west of the country. 'There is little doubt that its limit is set by the tree's intolerance of winter cold, a fact probably related to the late appearance and extension of the tree in the British Islands as on the north-west German Plain'(Godwin, 1956). Despite its ability to stand the low temperatures in the Himalayas, in Britain it does suffer from the effects of frost. H. J. Elwes and A. H. Henry give several instances of the tree being killed or damaged by frost, including some in the West of Scotland during the severe winter of 1837–8.

Yew woods seem to thrive better than any other trees on steep chalk downland slopes, and this seems to be their stronghold. Beech trees are successful in these conditions as well, and so are ash, but mainly when the slope is facing east or north and is thus moister, being protected from the prevailing winds and the full effect of the sun. The south- and west-facing slopes of Kingley Vale, and to a large extent the east-facing slope of the long Chilgrove ridge (brought into the reserve under lease in

32

1968) are the foundations of the yew forest, of the whole scientific reason for establishing the reserve. This is where the 'finest yew forest in Europe' exists.

Foliage of exposed yews at Kingley Vale frequently suffers and turns brown-red in the salt wind which sweeps in from the Channel. Those trees in wind streams on the spine of escarpments have a considerable lean away from the south-west. The yew grows on a wide variety of soil conditions, appearing to grow equally well on thin, hot chalk slopes, limestone pavement, fen peats with a high water-table, podsolic Bagshot and Headon beds (as in the New Forest), or carboniferous limestone as in Roudsea Wood and around Tintern in the Wye valley.

The distribution of yew has probably been seriously affected by the influence of man, since many early religious beliefs and pagan cultures centred around the tree. In Scotland distribution of the yew may be linked with its association with the early Christian Church (Cornish, 1946) or, from the late sixteenth century, its value as an ornamental tree (Hutchinson, 1890). It was also used as a boundary marker and as a tombstone in unconsecrated ground. The yew forms woodlands with closed canopy, particularly on steep valley sides or escarpment slopes, as at Dovedale and on the Kentish, Surrey, Sussex and Dorset downs. In the past, the yew has suffered at the hands of iron smelters as much as the oak, but unlike the oak was not replaced when its usefulness for bow-wood had vanished in the seventeenth century. Its present reasonable proliferation is due to the relaxation from time to time of various grazing pressures on the marginal land of steep and hilly slopes.

Age of the Yew

Much interest centres around the age of yews, since in many cases they are our only living link with history. It is tempting as one stands beneath a gnarled and ancient tree to suppose that it was standing thus a thousand years before. 'If only it could talk!' Many people who come to Kingley Vale *want* to believe that the old trees forming the grove are at least a thousand years old. Frequently they will offer this information, only looking to me for confirmation. In fact I have to disappoint them, though five hundred years is often an acceptable alternative to their sense of occasion. It is true that the trees, with their majestic spreading crowns, deeply fluted or fissured trunks and massive limbs do look older than they are. But five hundred years is the most that they could be. In general there are relatively few large yews other than in churchyards, which makes

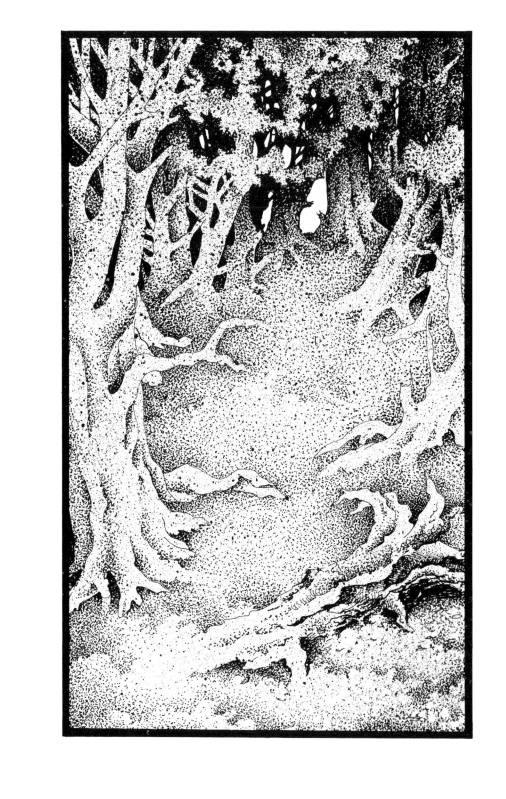

the natural grove in Kingley Vale particularly valuable. On the basis of ring counts from other trees, Dr A. S. Watt (1926) estimated the age of these yews to be much higher than our own estimates.

There are several different calculations for assessing the age of yew trees. One calculation gives 24 rings to the inch for old yews; another gives 28 for close-grained yew. H. L. Edlin (1958) gives 20 rings to the inch as a reasonable estimate for the Crowhurst yew (now a hollow shell 33 feet in circumference). Borings made into a selection of the Kingley Vale trees (Newbould, 1960) gave 10–20 rings to the inch for the younger trees, falling to 50 rings to the inch for the older trees, indicating an age of 500 years for the trees in the 5-foot diameter class. On this basis it should be possible for the very large trees such as the Crowhurst yew to be over 1000 years old.

However, there are many pitfalls. J. Lowe (1897) gives instances of yews that are supposedly one tree, but which in reality may be two or more individuals which have started life close together and whose trunks have coalesced. There are many yews like this at Kingley Vale. In the younger woods on the slopes they can be seen to be growing in family groups, usually three to six trees of about 80 years standing close to one another, showing how they had originally sprung from beneath the same bush of juniper or hawthorn. When they get to the age of 500 or even 250 years, several in the group will be touching, a few more years and the trunks will begin to grow together. Eventually one hoary old tree apparently occupies the site. Cut him down, however, and all the trunks will be found in the cross-section. I have one such section in my study, doing duty as a coffee table. It came from a tree felled near Bow Hill to make way for beech plantations. It has a circumference of 9 feet and is 187 years old, but there are clearly defined centres which started life $1\frac{1}{2}$ and $3\frac{1}{2}$ inches apart respectively. Another cross-section contains no less than seven different trees, the circumference of the whole being 46 inches. The circumference of the smallest is $8\frac{1}{2}$ inches and the largest is 21 inches, but they are all 46 years of age. From the outward appearance there was nothing to suggest that this 46-inch tree was not one 46-year-old individual. There are some very large trees too, which are in the process of joining into one. The wood of the yew seems more 'fluid' than other trees, in that it can flow around obstacles and envelop them more readily. Frequently a branch from another tree is found to pierce the branch or even trunk of another, the host accepting the neighbour and the two joining inseparably into one. Often a yew will advance upon another species and, if its neighbour is small enough, will flow completely around and enclose the stem. In this way large flints, too, can be enclosed. Sometimes the growth of a tree will slow up as it attains old age, producing as many as 80 rings to the inch.

The record for slow growth must go to a yew dug up in an Irish bog, which during the last 300 years of its life had put on 100 rings to the inch. I have found one which had 80 rings to the inch. This was a tree of exactly 2 inches diameter which had been stunted beneath its brothers and sisters. They had achieved varying success in life too, although all were exactly 80 years of age. They all grew in a rough circle, like a family seated around a 5-foot-wide circular table, except for the 'runt' who was underneath the table. Their diameters in inches were as follows: 2, $5\frac{1}{2}$, $7\frac{3}{4}$, $11\frac{1}{4}$ and $15\frac{1}{2}$. The latter had all the sun and possibly the benefit of the downhill drainage too. The group were on a north-facing slope on the far side of Bow Hill, just off the reserve. Many yews had been cut down on this slope, in a long narrow strip adjoining cattle pasture. Most were in this age-group and they all showed extreme ranges of size. It is thought that a tree with a diameter of 12 inches can safely be regarded as being 56 years old. But those in avenues or standing as individuals can afford to put on much girth at the expense of height and they may nearly double this width.

Luckily, J. Lowe visited Kingley Vale some time before 1897 and recorded the following valuable note, first quoting from *Longman's Magazine* of 1883.

'Tradition would seem to contain nothing incredible when it asserts that the yews on Kinglye Bottom, near Chichester, were on their present site when the sea-kings from the North landed on the coast of Sussex'. Had he said that 'Yews were there' the statement would have been accurate but that 'the yews' meaning those still existing were then in being, is too large a demand on our credulity as there is no tree at that place which exceeds 15.4 ft in girth or possibly about five hundred years in age.

Today there is no tree at Kingley Vale of girth greater than 20 feet 4 inches. A list of the biggest trees is given in the Appendix, p. 172.

The Yew in History

The derivation of the word *yew* seems obscure. Dr Johnson thought it was derived from the Anglo-Saxon *ip* or Welsh *yw*. If so, it is the only British tree to have retained a Celtic name. The Gaelic equivalent is *iubhar*, anglicised and pronounced as *ure*. *Yew* in Welsh means 'it is', being the third person present indicative of the auxiliary verb *bod*, to be. There are considerable variations in spellings over the centuries: *eu, ew* (Chaucer), *eugh* (Spenser), *iun, yugh, yeugh, yewe, yowe, you, ewgh, ugh, u, ewe*. Another view is that the word derives from the Celtic *jubar*, pronounced yewar and meaning 'the evergreen head'. The earliest written reference in Anglo-Saxon is the spelling *iuu* found in a seventh-century Epiral manuscript. The Latin generic name *taxus* may derive from *toxicum*, poison, or from a Greek word meaning 'to arrange', since the leaves are somewhat neatly arranged either side of the twigs. The ancient belief that evergreen trees were associated with immortality may have begun long before the Romans' custom of depositing their cypress trees in a burial tomb ('funebri indicio est fores posita' – Pliny). Another early reference is by Sir Thomas Browne (1658): ' . . . funeral pyre consisted of sweet fuel, cypress, fir, larix, yew and trees perpetually verdant, silent expressions of their surviving "hopes" '. There is reason to believe that the first churches were placed in or near groves of yews (the yew is one of Britain's few native evergreen trees, the others being Scots pine and juniper). The Victorians thought so, at least, noting too that the first churches were sited on pagan temples of worship.

> When Augustine was sent by Gregory the Great to preach Christianity in Britain, he was enjoined to purify and not to destroy the temples of Pagan worship; and it is not unlikely that the very presence of the venerable yews would prove an attraction to these sites. The old Pagans, like the modern heathens loved to place trees around the place of worship (*Magazine of Natural History*, 1836).

Lowe, however, discounts this theory, observing that Ancient Britons placed their temples in open spaces and not among trees.

Henry Coote (1878) described how, for the Romans, the yew gave passage of the soul to its new abode. So, ever since the introduction of Christianity into this country, yew has continued to adorn the last resting-place of the body, which the soul has left. John Evelyn, writing in his famous *Sylva* in the seventeenth century, suggested that 'the best reason that can be given why the yew was planted in churchyards is that branches of it were carried in procession of Palm Sunday instead of Palms.' In William Caxton's lecture for Palm Sunday ('Directions for Keeping Feasts all the Year') he says: 'Wherefore Holy Churche this day making the solemn processyon, in memory of the processyon that Cryst made this day. But for the eucheson that we have none Olyves that bereth grene leef, algate therefore we take Ewe instead of palm and olyve, and beren about in processyon, and so is this day called Palm

Sunday'. In 1898 Lowe reported that yew trees in East Kent were called palms, while John Brady in *Clavis Calendaria* describes how

> Among our superstitious forefathers the palm tree or its substitute, box or yew, were solemnly blessed, and some of their branches burnt to ashes and used by priests on Ash Wednesday of the following year, while other boughs were gathered and distributed among the pious who bore them about in their numerous processions, a practice which was continued in the country until the second year of Edward VI, when it was abolished as superstitious.

For many centuries yew wood supplied the raw material for Britain's strategic weapon, the longbow. It is widely supposed that yews were planted in churchyards for bow-wood, but what are the facts? In 1483 Richard III ordered a general plantation of yews for the use of archers, and Elizabeth I encouraged the planting of the yew tree in churchyards, where they could be both carefully tended and kept from poisoning cattle. The early Victorians planted the tree in cemeteries, partly from a sense of occasion and history and, in some cases, from the odd belief that the roots delved deep into the earth and cleaned the ground, while the thick overhanging leaves acted like a giant 'air-wick', since they 'cleaned the air of the noxious gases arising from the graves'. Other Victorians discounted that bow-wood came from churchyards. G. A. Hansard in *The Book of Archery*, 1841, was one of them:

> Is it not absurd to suppose that men would plant, within these contracted bounds, a single tree of such slow growth, that in the space of a century its height and substance are scarcely sufficient to supply half a dozen bow staves, while numbers were courting the bow man's axe on every hillside? The piety, or as some men choose to style it, the superstition, of our ancestors would have been decidedly opposed to the application of wood reared within consecrated ground to any such purpose. Not within consecrated ground only, but even the domain of the clergy. When Henry IV issued his commission to Nicholas Frost, the royal bowyer, to enter upon the lands of private individuals and cut down yew or any other wood for the public service, he expressly forbids his trespassing on estates belonging to any religious order. Every yew tree growing within the united church-yards of England and Wales, admitting they could have been renewed five times in the course of a century, would not have produced one fiftieth part of the bows required for military supplies.

Other kings had differing views, for Charles VII of France ordered yew to be planted in all the churchyards of Normandy in order to supply the crossbow manufacturers. As early as A.D. 684 it was obviously venerated in France, since the charter for a new church to be built at Perone in Picardy contained a clause dictating the protection of a certain yew tree in the grounds. But whatever was thought about churchyard yews being used for bows, the fact remains that British yew was inferior to continental wood.

It was not until the oak began to be our principal forest tree in the construction of wooden battleships that the use of yew for military purposes declined. Homer and Virgil recorded that yew was one of the best woods for bows, and from then on an intricate knowledge of the properties of yew was gathered together, and foreign wood was proved many times to be superior. An enactment at the time laid down that merchants importing casks of wine had also to import staves or billets of yew wood from the same country. The English nation was built upon the longbow: it may almost be said that without yew wood there would never have been a British Commonwealth.

From the thirteenth century anyone with an annual income of less than 100 pence was obliged to have in his possession a bow and sharp arrows (blunt arrows if he lived in a Royal forest), which were inspected by military officials at regular intervals. Edward III, in a letter to the Sheriff of London in 1349, commanded them

> . . . to proclaim that every one of the said city, strong in body, at leisure times, on holidays, use in their recreation bows and arrows or piles and bolts and learn and exercise the art of shooting . . . and do not . . . apply themselves to the throwing of stones, wood or iron, hand-ball, foot-ball, bandy-ball, cambuck or cock fighting nor suchlike vain plays which have no profit in them.

Richard II passed an act compelling all servants to shoot. Edward IV proclaimed that every Englishman should have a bow of his own height made either of yew, wych-hazel, ash or laburnum. Anyone caught not practising on feast days would be fined a halfpenny. Richard III decreed a general planting of yew and a compulsory import of foreign staves. Queen Mary's reign fixed the price of bows, which had been in considerable dispute for a long while, as follows: a bow made of the best foreign wood, 6s 8d; for an inferior sort, 3s 4d; for a bow made of English yew, 2s. Even after the introduction of firearms in the fourteenth century, the bow continued to be the principal weapon of defence, being used at both Agincourt and Flodden Field.

By 1511 archery had become neglected throughout the land, so

Henry VIII decreed that '. . . every man, being the King's subject, not lame, decrepit or maimed, do use and exercise shooting with longbows, and also do have a bow and arrows ready continually in his home to use himself in shooting.' Every male child over the age of seven was to have a bow. In the reign of Philip and Mary this 'National Service' was continued, for from 1 May 1588 the well-to-do (those with estates valued at £1000 or over) were to keep 'thirty bows, thirty sheaf of arrows', while at the other end of the scale those having £5–£10 were to keep 'one long bow, one sheaf of arrows and steel cap or skull' – the penalty for non-compliance to be 10s per bow.

In Elizabeth's reign the yew bow was no longer such a common item, the stocks of wood, both at home and abroad, obviously having been depleted. Her Act of Bowyers ordained that every bowyer should have fifty bows made of elm, wych-hazel or ash. The last statute concerning yew wood was the '13th Elizabeth, Cap 14', directing that yew-wood staves be imported from the Hanse towns and other places. Again, the price of bows was fixed: 'Bows meet for men's shooting being outlandish, Yew of the best sort, not over the price of 6/8; bows meet for men's shooting of the second sort 3/4; bows for men, of a coarser sort called livery bows 2/0, bows being English Yew 2/0'. By then the tree had become so scarce that yew wood had to be shared around. For every bow of yew, a bowyer must have four of wych-hazel or elm, and they were forbidden to be kept by men under the age of seventeen.

By the seventeenth century, Evelyn in his *Sylva* was concerned at the lack of yew. 'Since the use of bows is laid aside amongst us, the propagation of the eugh is likewise quite forborn, but the neglect of it is to be deplored.' Thereafter longbows were kept alive by Lodges and Companies. By 1598 a description of London's Grub Street gives the somewhat familiar picture: '. . . inhabited of late years by bowyers, fletcher and bowstring makers [it] is now little occupied; archery giving place to a number of bowling alleys and dining houses, which in all places are increased and too much frequented.' This was also in part due to the enclosing of open spaces, 'for by closing in the common grounds our archers, for want of room to shoot abroad, creep into bowling-alleys and ordinary dining-houses, near home, where they have room enough to hazard their money at unlawful games.' In 1629 Charles I enforced the use of the longbow and part of his army at the beginning of the Civil War were so armed; the last record of the military use of the longbow was at the siege of Devizes under Cromwell.

The best bows were made of Spanish yew, English wood having too many 'pins' or small twigs embedded in the wood, which might cause fracture. In a treatise by Roger Ascham, 1545, the following advice on the purchase of bows appears:

> . . . every bowe is made of the boughe; the plante or the boole of the tree. The boughe commonly is verye knotty, and full of pinnes weak of small pithe; the plante is quick enough of cacte, it will plye and bow far afore it breaks and the boole is best. If you come into a shoppe and fynde a bowe that is small, long, heavie and strong, lying streighte, not wyndynge nor marred with knottes gaule, wyndeshake, wen, freat or pynche, bye that bowe on my warrant. As for hazell, elme, wyche and ash experience doth prove them to be mean for bowes and so to conclude, ewe of all other things is that whereof perfite shootings would have a bowe made.

Plantation yew would have yielded the best bow-wood, since the staves or billets were prepared by splitting into 6 or 8 equal segments a straight length of bole 6 feet in length. The cleaver billets were then shaped and tested for bending. Trees grown naturally on a site such as Kingley Vale would be ideal, for many of these, having grown together, have naturally drawn up straight like any other trees planted in close proximity to one another. French crossbows were also made of yew until the use of steel became commoner in the sixteenth century. Crossbows were inferior to longbows in battle, due to their slow operation: only three bolts could be discharged in the time that it took an English archer to deliver ten to twelve arrows. The battle of Crécy in 1346 was won partly through the superiority of longbows.

A Potent Poison

It is a well-known fact that the yew is poisonous, though it is also believed to have medicinal properties. To most large mammals including man it is often, but not always, deadly. Dead, dried leaves are thought to be most poisonous, and at Kingley Vale various bullocks, heifers and a few horses have been killed by straying into the reserve area in the past, taking mouthfuls of these as they passed along the trackways. Nowadays people are more careful with their horses, and farmers' fences are stronger and better maintained, but even so in the past fifteen years there have been six cases of domestic stock breaking into the yew forest – only one of these was fatal, two heifers dying shortly after. The curious fact about the poison is that it does not always affect mammals, and the secret seems to be that an animal can acquire

immunity. Yew used to be fed to cattle, regularly, on the Continent.

Lowe, in 1897, made an exhaustive inquiry into the history of yew poisoning up to that date, when the trees were more common and accessible than they are today. He recorded how an old shepherd on Box Hill in Surrey told him that his cows frequently ate the leaves, but never suffered any ill-effects from it as they were turned out daily and therefore never took a harmful quantity. When they have been shut up, and especially when the ground is covered with snow, the result is very different, as they eat greedily of the only green vegetation visible. Lowe relates that 'In January 1823, in a deep snow, Messrs. Woodward & Chelmsford turned out three healthy horses into a small close adjoining which was a yew tree. In three hours they were found dead with yew in their stomachs'. Again: 'Master Wells, minister at Adderbury, seeing some boys breaking boughs from the yew tree in the churchyard thought himself much injured. To prevent the like trespasses he sent one presently to cut downe the tree and to bring it in . . . his cowes began to feed upon the leaves and two of them within a few hours dyed. A just reward.' But, given constant access, domestic stock did not suffer: 'There are many trees in pastures and fences', reported the Victorian *New Planter's Kalendar*, 'which are uniformly browsed by sheep and cattle without doing them any injury whatever. In extensive yew plantations cattle were admitted without any evil consequences to themselves, though the trees were browsed to the very boughs.'

This was the case on Kingley Vale and surrounding downlands in the 1920s and 1930s. Mr Fred Longman of Lavant, a shepherd boy just after the First World War, recalled how sheep often wandered among the yew but did not trouble to eat it. A Danish experiment of the last century showed that although horses were particularly prone to poisoning, this did not occur when the yew leaves were mixed with two or three times the quantity of oats. In Germany, in the mountains of Hanover and Hesse, the peasants fed their cattle with branches of yew during the winter, beginning with a small quantity and gradually increasing the amount.

Although the deer of Kingley Vale have never been known to suffer ill-effects, a fallow deer yearling in Epping Forest was killed when it browsed entirely on one tree which it came across. The five New Forest ponies which were turned out into a 17-acre paddock in the reserve in 1971–5 undoubtedly ate yew leaves from time to time, since there were some small trees that I did not discover until after the ponies had done so. They did not strip the trees, but ate small quantities every now and then. However, the three donkeys turned out into another paddock of 3

43

acres in 1976 did not attempt ever to browse on yew leaves or bark – even though they were more crowded, lived through a cold, wet winter when they practically denuded their paddock of bushes including privet (supposedly poisonous) and when one animal accidentally climbed into a small enclosure surrounding a large yew.

Lowe records that 'deer, sheep, goats, hares and rabbits eat yew without harm. Cattle and horses, if not freshly turned out do not eat sufficiently to cause any evil.' An experiment in France by one Charles Connevin in 1892 showed that the quantity of leaves needed to kill various mammals was as follows:

(per kilogramme of live weight per animal)

horse	2g	cow	10g
ass or mule	1.6g	pig	3g
sheep	10g	dog	8g
goat	12g	rabbit	20g

I am very surprised by Lowe's statement that 'birds of all kinds are poisoned by the leaves'. He reported that pheasants are apparently the greatest sufferers. In 1892 fifteen pheasants were killed by eating yew leaves at Hillington Hall. The gamekeeper noted that these birds, which had recently been disturbed by shooting, had taken to perching in the yew trees and were apt to pick at the leaves as a change of diet. Although 10,000 pheasants were reared annually in the farmland surrounding Kingley Vale I never once heard complaints by any of the gamekeepers of this disaster befalling their birds, all of which had access to yews in their home wood as well as in the reserve. Birds which live out their lives within the yew trees, however, do tend to be much smaller than average, and are not particularly tasty to eat either. W. B. Tegetmeier in *Pheasants*, 1881, after an exhaustive study of these birds, regarded as unquestionable the fact that they were sometimes poisoned by yew, quoting Professor R. V. Tuson: 'One of a number of pheasants, suspected to have been poisoned was sent to me for analysis. In the craw I discovered yew leaves, also in the gizzard, and by its odour distinct evidence of its existence in the intestines. I reported that, in my opinion, the bird was killed through the eating of yew leaves.'

There is a considerable history of the yew poisoning humans, though as far as I know there has been no case in Kingley Vale. In *De Bello Gallico* Caesar records that Cativolcus, king of the Eburones, committed suicide by drinking yew juice. If hemlock was an alternative for the

Romans and yew juice was considered as effective, then it gives one a new respect for taxin poison!

Virgil thought that Corsican honey was tainted if not poisoned by yew pollen. I have heard bee-keepers say the same, but if this is true it is fortunate that in our country at least the tree is in flower too early (February–March) for much pollen to be collected. Pliny describes how the juice which he called toxica was used to tip arrows, making them deadly, but this idea must be false since the poison acts on the stomach and intestine.

As with many plants which have a distinctive role, the yew has been accredited not only with the power to do harm, but to do good as well. The Roman Emperor Claudius assured his subjects through the Senate that yew poison was a sure antidote to adders' bites. This would be invaluable if it were true in a place like Kingley Vale. And there may be a hint of truth in it, for the effect of the slowing of the pulse rate and the general acquiescent nature of taxin could slow the rate of venom distribution throughout the body. In the seventeenth century taxin was recommended as an antidote to rabies.

The question above all concerning the yew tree, which in my experience of talking to many thousands of people is of most interest, is that regarding the berries. Are they or are they not poisonous? Lowe has the last word:

> Every part of the plant is more or less poisonous, with the exception of the red mucilage surrounding the ripe seeds. It is necessary to emphasise this, as so many random and careless assertions have been made on the subject. There is probably no point on which so many errors and discrepancies have arisen as on the question of the character of the *fruit*. This consists of a small nut surrounded by red fleshy pulp and having in its interior an almond flavoured kernel. The pulp is quite harmless in character, but it cannot be too widely known that the nut is distinctly injurious and in large quantities poisonous. Numerous instances have been recorded of fatal results ensuing from having eaten the berries, which from the sweetness of the mucilage are very attractive to children.

The herbalist Gerard, talking, one imagines, solely about the red pulp and not the kernel, said: 'When I was yonge and went to schoole, divers of my schoolefellows and likewise myselfe did eat our fils of this tree, and have not only slept under the shadow thereof, but among the branches also without any hurt at all and that not one time but many times. . . . Daily experience shows it to be true that the yew tree in

45

England is not poisonous.' The last sentence is a curious statement indeed, since a man of Gerard's experience must surely have known about the leaves poisoning cattle. His reference to sleeping under the tree with impunity is in answer to a legend attributed to the Greeks about the shade of yews being poisonous, a legend which I too have disproved.

At least two cases of seed poisoning were recorded in the last century. One person died comatose four hours after the berries had been eaten and the other nineteen days afterwards, the bowels being severely inflamed. In 1870 the *Medical Times and Gazette* recorded a death by berry eating, and two more were reported in the *Gardeners' Chronicle* for 1881, one being a mentally deficient patient in Sussex County Asylum who had eaten large quantities of berries and was found dead. A post-mortem revealed irritation of the stomach and intestines. At Droxford in Hampshire, 20 miles from Kingley Vale, a boy of three who had eaten berries and pips was poisoned. Presumably he had bitten the nuts, as one does sometimes when eating grapes. The doctor records: 'When first seen he was just recovering from a convulsion; he was semi-comatose, but could be roused; the skin was cold and clammy; breathing difficult; pupils dilated and slight attempts at vomiting.' In 1950 Dr Kathleen Harding, walking on the downs near Heyshott, demonstrated the, to her, apparent harmlessness of the yew pips by crunching several and swallowing them. It is not known exactly how many she ate, but she is known to have done this several times and to have suffered no ill-effects. I have eaten large quantities of red arils, always being careful to discard the pips.

Unlike in old Gerard's day, children no longer eat the arils. They are quite certain that the red pulp is deadly, and judging by the litter returns it seems that crisps, Tic-Tacs and Coke are considered superior in taste. The birds and foxes no longer have any competition from humans. In the past, humans have experimented with the leaves with unfortunate results. Evelyn records the fate of some children in Manchester on 25 March 1774:

> Three children of a labouring man were killed by taking a small quantity of fresh leaves on the recommendation of an ignorant person for the cure of worms. A spoonful of dried leaves was first given, followed by a drink of sour buttermilk. This produced no ill effect, and two days afterwards the same dose of fresh leaves was adminis-tered, causing the death of all three children. Two hours after the leaves were given they began to be uneasy; were chilly and listless,

yawned much and frequently stretched out their limbs. The eldest vomited a little and complained of abdominal pains. The others expressed no signs of pains. No agonies accompanied their dissolution; no swelling of the abdomen ensued; and after death they had the appearance of being in a placid sleep.

Since then it has been proved that dead leaves contain taxin as much as fresh leaves. Other deaths recorded give faintness, convulsions resembling epilepsy, and bleeding of the stomach as symptoms of the poison. Lowe conducted experiments upon himself with taxin poison.

The tracings of the pulse show beyond doubt that it is a cardiac tonic of no mean value. The heart's action is decreased in frequency by small doses such as one-twentieth to one-eighth grain at the same time that the cardiac pressure is distinctly increased. These effects I have found to be durable. In large doses it generally depresses the heart's action. On the whole it contrasts favourably with digitalis and convallaria and is worthy of more extended observation.

To conclude, the yew forest provides a range of interests for most of us. For some it may be the pursuit of scientific knowledge and the chance of some unusual finding; for others, the discovery of beauty, majesty and artistic inspiration. Many a painting and poem has resulted from a visit here, as well as an increasing number of scientific papers.

Even the casual visitor is likely to be touched, however lightly, by feelings ranging from joy to curiosity to fear, although he may not even be aware of the fact until later. Be warned – your visit to the 'sinister and fantastic forest' will leave its mark!

The Animals

Deer

There are two species of deer resident in Kingley Vale, although their presence is probably comparatively recent. Fallow were recorded before the 1940s, but there were few of them, and roe have only recently spread – mainly because of the upsurge of scrub, yew woodland and nearby beech plantations which provide cover and food.

The fallow deer is the larger of the two, being about 3 feet high at the shoulder and weighing about 12 stone. The usual fallow has a summer coat of reddish brown, covered with large white spots, with a flaring white target (rump) divided by the black tail hair. However, variations do occur, and there are some all-black fallow, and some all-white. The winter coat is a muted uniform greyish brown. The male's antlers are the large spreading 'palmate' ones. These are shed in May; new antlers grow each year, progressively larger with age, and are covered in the soft stage of growth with 'velvet' (a covering of soft, furry skin). The velvet is cleaned off by the animal fraying (rubbing) them against low branches in about mid-August, although as the animal gets older he tends to cast his antlers a bit earlier – perhaps April – and clean the velvet off the new growth a bit later – perhaps September. The antlers are easily damaged while in velvet, and the fallow buck is very careful of them. The antlers continue to develop until the fallow is about nine years old, when they tend to start regressing.

The roe deer is a much smaller animal. The buck is only 2 feet high at the shoulder, and the whole build and appearance is much finer than that of the heavier fallow. The roe's summer coat is of a foxy reddish brown, the target being pale and not visibly marked. The winter coat is of a duller colour, but the winter target becomes white and flares conspicuously in alarmed flight.

The antler growth of the roe buck is completely different from that of the fallow. The roe's antlers are short, neat, spiky affairs, which can deal a lethal knife-like wound when fighting. They cast their antlers in October or November; the new velvet-covered ones start to grow

48

immediately, and fraying and cleaning occurs in May. The antlers are at their best in about the sixth year, and thicken and regress from then on.

Fallow deer mate in October, and the young, called fawns, are born in May–June. The roe rut occurs in July–August and their young (kids) are born also in May–June. It is believed that 'delayed implantation' occurs – this allows the roe to mate at the height of condition when food is plentiful and for the young to be born at a time of warmth, and when food is again plentiful for the nursing doe.

The slots (footprints) of the fallow are larger and heavier, those of the roe being small and dainty with more pointed cleaves. It is easy for the inexperienced person to confuse the slot of young fallow with that of the roe, while the seasoned observer can pick up the characteristics of individual animals.

The stock of the fallow now on the reserve is so cosmopolitan that it would be impossible even to suggest its origin. As everywhere, there are some colour variations. When I arrived in 1963 there had recently been a report in the local paper of a 'black buck' on Bow Hill. It had been seen by the Cowdray Hunt, among others. Never having seen wild deer – except for a carted red deer hind which walked into our garden one day in Norfolk and lay down on the lawn, taking little notice when twenty couple of hounds surrounded and licked it after chasing it for ten miles – I was very keen to see them. I knew that the fallow rut occurred in October, usually about the twenty-fifth. But as early as the tenth, having wandered towards evening among the thorn thickets seeing nothing but slots, I suddenly heard the groaning of a rutting buck. This sounded so much like a pig grunting that I was almost fooled. On coming closer, upwind and creeping quietly through the almost black thickets of yew and thorn on the plateau, I knew that it was a sound that I had never heard before. It was a black sound, full of our dark memories of the night forest. This was not a fact to be analysed or glibly described for science: it was the intangible emotion of an animal. So often I saw wild animals running away, or eating, or moving about, actions which excited little empathy. Now as I crouched beneath the yews the buck stood before me, a mere twenty paces off, and I felt part of him, and part of the forest.

I decided then to get a little closer. In order not to frighten him from his rutting stand where he was parading back and forth in a small area of some ten paces or so, I imitated his groan. I got it right on the second note, not at first realising how deep the sound was. I imagined that he would merely think I was another buck and forgive my crackling of leaves and twigs underfoot. But the effect was electrifying. He stopped dead, though I could not yet see him for night was nearly upon me. On my fourth or fifth note there was the slightest sound and I was somewhat alarmed to see, in a clear patch of sky ahead, a great set of antlers widening as they came towards me. He had moved over twenty paces in a second or two and now stood before me, a few paces distant, only dimly outlined and from my crouching position looking very large. I dared not move. I had no idea whether fallow bucks were dangerous or not, but with this one standing over me I feared that they might be. Two minutes passed, and the silence that passed between us consolidated that tenuous bridge I had formed between his world and mine. I wanted to engage him in combat, or touch him. But then the moment was sliding away, for he had turned and was vanishing back the way he had come, and then he had gone and it was all over. Was this the 'great black buck' described in the newspaper report? That he was a 'great buck', a buck of six years, seemed fairly certain by the size of those antlers.

Shortly afterwards I saw him again, and the daylight sighting confirmed that he had a sooty brown rump with no white markings and general colouring which was almost black, especially as he was then wet with October fog. His antlers were not of the normal horn colour either, but were as sooty as antlers hung a hundred years in a smoky room. His kingdom was the hilltop, the highest point of the plateau, a secret jungle of thorn, gorse and hidden grass glades. He had thrashed whitebeams, thorns, yews and gorse, sallow willow and even brambles to mark his territory. One thorn bush was peeled of bark all down one side, as though it had been run over by a vehicle, its crown of twigs broken up. A smaller territory was held by a three-year-old dappled buck on the western side. He would stand out in the open watching the empty grassy meadows below, running up and down the earthwork there when restlessness overcame him. His groan was lighter, his antlers only half the size, but one day I saw him with just one doe, following her around among the planted beech trees.

The great buck groaned for ten days or more among the misty autumnal woods. One evening I lay in wait for him again; it was the nineteenth day of the month. I was not disappointed. He had been groaning in the morning, hidden in a blanket of mist. By early evening he had begun again, after a calm and sunny day of St Luke's Little Summer. The grove of yews on the hill was shot through with horizontal shafts of red sun, and into those he and his does came, not just one or two but six, skipping and trotting lightly around him. For a moment he was hidden by them as they closed around his heavy black body, then they were ahead, then to the side, red sun flickering all over their dappled backs. As they darted about, he plodded, heavy shouldered, head thrown back, rasping out the deep snoring groans, his neck as thick as a man's thigh, antlers encompassing half the space across his black back. Those antlers could now be seen at their best. They were magnificent. He seemed unaware of what was happening beyond this haven, but the does were watching everything and kept looking in my direction even though I, ignoring completely a spider that crawled back and forth over my ear, was as still as one of the yew branches I leant upon. Eventually the little band of trysting animals, weaving in and out of the tree trunks, died away with the sun into some other hidden grove. Shortly after, the autumn rains came and this rut was over. One night in November I was plodding home across the hill along a narrow muddy track, when there was a crash as something rushed the gorse-brakes and the great black buck landed with a squelch of mud and water in front of me. Something had disturbed him into this headlong flight. He was as black as the devil and his eye rolled at me in that moment before he vanished back through the gorse.

Snow makes it much easier to get an idea of how many deer are present. At other times one can look for slots, 'galleries' (paths) and entries, but each slot must be individually identified and remembered and this is not always possible when the slots are, for the most part, foiled in grass. But in the January snow a clear impression was left of the buck and his six does, down in the bottom of the valley, well sheltered from northerly winds. I had no record of deer ever being there before. The snow was six inches deep, and the deer had pawed into it to find grass and moss. Thereafter the fallow galleries became regular and were used in the valley until the spring, when the deer moved out into safer ground away from visitors and their dogs. In such an enclosed place – with no long straight rides to view deer at a distance as they cross into or out of the feeding ground, and with no wide open moorlands where they could be observed by telescope from a vantage point – the main methods of counting and recording numbers are by keeping a record of the amount and extent of browsing, the presence of droppings and the development of browse-lines, and by tracking and keeping a log of individuals' slots.

The great buck's were recognisable by their large size. He also turned out his feet more than the does, and one fore cleave was almost curled around the front of its neighbour on the same foot. His slot sunk nearly twice as far into the mud as the does' did since he probably weighed about 150 lb compared to the does' weight of say 100 lb or under. He

FALLOW DEER

became elusive, nocturnal. His lodging was the yew and hawthorn thicket on the plateau. One of his galleries was diagonally down the western side of the main valley; another was in the opposite direction, along the crest of Bow Hill to the enclosure on the ridge. But in late winter he vanished, and then quite by chance I came upon him in the middle of April. It was a calm evening, and the bluebells were out in the sycamore and ash grove next to the reserve. Among the tree crowns were five deer crowns; five fallow bucks were feeding together in a group just before dusk (a fortnight later they had all dropped their antlers). This area has always been used by the bucks at such times. One year there were seven bucks nearby, grazing on meadows hard by the felled wood. It is also the place that sick or maimed bucks will make for at any time of year.

By 1969 the fallow population numbered 14 and was beginning to make itself obvious: in much of the valley along the western side the tips of young ashes were browsed off or taller saplings snapped in half so that the tip could be reached.

In November 1970, 19 does and one buck were seen. On one night of snow in 1971 a herd of 16 were tracked when they approached the reserve boundary from the west, ran straight down through forest to the valley where they roamed up and down all night, taking ash, bramble, yew, grass and herbs and the occasional holly and dogwood leaves, before fleeing back the way they had come at dawn. When the snow had gone a watch was kept, and sure enough the same herd appeared in the late evening advancing on a broad front, trotting hungrily straight back to the valley. In the next year they did not bother to move out by day, but couched half way up the slope on small platforms scraped out of the soft earth. They were sheltered from rain as far as possible, out of the wind, and escape routes led to all points of the compass.

The visual effect of the herd having spent the night feeding in Cp. 8 was as if a herd of bullocks had been penned there. This was good work as far as the management of the reserve was concerned because the regrowth from bushes always had to be cleared, and the grass was getting long and rank, and beginning to shade out more 'interesting' herbs. Also, the brambles which had been spreading in rings around many of the outlying yews were being contained.

At first, the herds fed by night mainly along the yew woodland edge (there is little or no food inside a pure yew grove except for a few ash saplings as described earlier). The outside trees lost much of their lower greenery, and the twigs became stunted and bald. This browsing line slowly descended the hill on the far western boundary during 1972–3, moving south until they crossed the dividing line of the centre valley track, when a completely new feeding ground was opened up. Yew saplings as yet untouched except by the occasional hare or rabbit were cropped so close that eventually they began to die out. Even de-barking of yews was observed. By 1975 there were 33 does in the reserve, though many of them moved constantly out and across the boundary.

There was a problem, however. We were trying to see about encouraging juniper scrub again, the great ancestor of the yew woodland. By 1971 the 36 seedling junipers which I had been studying since 1964, measuring their growth rates and general welfare, had been frayed by the deer during the rut and when they were cleaning velvet. The effect was catastrophic to the much cherished and precious shrubs, which were already becoming something of a rarity in Britain. In 1969 there was one fallow buck within the main reserve area and in 1976 there were three; they just loved the smell, size and spinginess of junipers for trying out the strength of their neck muscles, for testing the spread and width of their new antlers or removing the tatters of velvet, and for generally exhilarating in the sauna-style whippiness of the needles. I watched a young three-year buck becoming joyously angry with one of the best shrubs that had grown from 10 inches to 6 feet in my time. I puffed up the slope shouting and had practically to hit him on the rump before he moved over. But he was back at it the next day. This 'tameness' in the rut, incidentally, is well known among observers of fallow. Most animals remain reasonably wary, but the occasional buck appears to be living in another world. I have, every year, been able to call them to me, but a friend reports how on one occasion in nearby Marden forest a young buck walking along a footpath all but bumped into him as he stood out in the open in broad daylight. A well-known deer expert in the New Forest is reputed to have driven up to one and hung his hat on its antlers, before it bolted.

While on the subject of the rut, some nasty and rather bizarre fates have befallen one or two bucks here at rutting time. In 1973 a three-year-old, an outlier, was using an old stretch of rabbit-netting on Bow Hill as a fraying stock. His top tines became well meshed and entangled therein, and he tore the netting off the top holding wire and out of the ground as well. Backing away, tugging more and more wire with him, he retreated in a semi-circle; coming back to the fence further down, he tripped or fell over it and found that he had turned his burden around a strainer post. Gradually his ten-yard 'lead' became shorter as he wound it up. Eventually he was hard and fast against the post. At this point, at least a day having elapsed to judge by the churned ground, someone may have appeared. In wild panic he made a last desperate lunge and and snapped off one antler, which released him.

Another buck on some farmland near the reserve took exception to a polythene cover draped over a stack of bales. It must have made a satisfying rattling noise as he waded into the attack one evening. Unfortunately, the opponent would not give way. Working around the stack the buck tore off a lengthening strip of polythene, until after two revolutions at least he had got himself free – though still attached firmly to 50 yards of yard-wide ribbon. Off he went into the country, pursued by his terrifying enemy which snapped and snarled at his heels, jerking back his head each time it caught up in a fence, blowing ahead in strong winds and completely confusing him. I saw him in the middle of a barley field. The black polythene lay like a coiled eel over the stalks, idly turning this way and that in the wind. I got within several yards when the buck rose and lunged off over the corn, the polythene whipping and flapping with an alarming noise behind. Much later, I found the length of polythene draped over the trunks of small yew trees in the wood. On another occasion a deer dragged 20 yards of tangled baler twine into this same place and managed to free itself on the sharp projections of small dead branches.

But there were more serious injuries. Although the Deer Act had recently been passed outlawing certain sizes of shot as used from smooth-bore guns, people still used them on the deer. It was after all far more convenient for a person with a gun loaded up ready for rabbits or pigeons to fire a snap-shot at a departing deer, than to go to the trouble of looking through pockets for the correct sized SG – or even to bother to buy them at all, with all the necessary but highly inconvenient business which that entails under the Firearms Act. A fallow buck of one year was found reeling into thick cover with festering wounds to the skull. A post-mortem revealed twenty pellets of No. 5 shot embedded in the skull. A roebuck's skull found in thick cover retained two pellets of No. 4 shot. A fallow doe was seen staggering about and was eventually found dead on the reserve with pellet wounds in its haunches. There were obviously more, judging from reports. It may be that many of the injuries were caused by poachers who, at that time, found it easy to drive about over the hills in cars in dry weather.

Fox snares take their toll too. These are set everywhere throughout the countryside to keep the fox population at a level compatible with rearing pheasants on a large scale. Before condemning out of hand the use of snares it is as well to remember that pheasants offer a good source of food from hedgerows and shelter-belts which otherwise would be unproductive, and which might well be grubbed out on a large scale if there was not an incentive for preserving them. On the other hand snares are horribly cruel, strangling an animal fairly quickly but with great pain and fear judging by the amount of leaping about that occurs. With deer it can be more traumatic. They step into snares and may then drag around the lump of wood to which the snare is attached, like a ball and chain, or if it is anchored to the ground, tear off the loop. These snares cannot easily be opened, so that once fixed on a deer's foot they restrict the flow of blood and after a while the foot drops off. I found one of these severed feet on the reserve and it is in my possession now, complete with loop. In 1974 a three-legged buck was seen in the 'sick quarters', but it was running well and had a good head. It was later shot on a neighbouring estate.

Dogs are difficult to contain on a nature reserve. People are allowed to bring their dogs but are requested to keep them under control. For most, this means keeping them on a lead. Unfortunately, many owners can never believe that 'MY' dog would do any damage, even as it returns panting with exhaustion and with debris round its mouth.

Every warden knows the sickening feeling of being unable to stop a dog running amuck, whether it is among terns, stone curlews or deer. People may say 'Well, if you have so many deer does it matter if they are chased?' To me it matters if one deer out of fifty is chased into a barbed-wire fence. The anguish and prolonged pain suffered by one such doe, which I found still alive after being chased by a dog, was enough to make me wary of dogs for a long time. The doe was hanging upside down with all four legs entangled in the top and middle strands of a barbed-wire fence which she had hit diagonally. Normally, fallow can slip these fences easily by jumping carefully in a flattened posture through bottom and middle strands. She had struck the top wire with all four legs, trod down to below the middle strand as she rolled over the top to the other side, thus leaving her legs on the wrong side. She swung on like a pendulum and was trapped upside down. She had to be destroyed and her legs cut off to remove the carcass. Many times have I seen roe or fallow running with a dog in pursuit. The breeds of dog seen have ranged through a wide variety – Jack Russell, Labrador, Doberman pinscher, Dalmation, Afghan and red setter being the most usual. Such dogs may, of course, kill other wildlife, a brood of pheasants taking but moments to despatch; they may also cause damage to farming stock.

Fallow fawns have in recent years been dropped in the valley, though their normal nursery is the much thicker scrub on the plateau and the impenetrable plantation of young beech mixed with scrub to the north.

56

June is the most usual month, but once I watched one being born as late as September. The doe was lying down on her side in an unusual attitude, her neck outstretched. All at once she raised herself on her haunches and the forefeet of a fawn could be seen coming out of the vagina. She rose from this kneeling position, her tail standing up and her neck again pushed forward. She remained like this, then walked forward after a minute and again pushed. A slimy, greyish black bag seemed to cover the fawn, although this was probably only the remains of the water. Slowly it slipped down, hanging in mid-air as the doe walked around the glade, attached by mucous and strings of the afterbirth. Its touchdown was gentle, but final, and the doe turned to greet her young one, licking its face and ears and back until its head began to wobble on its skinny neck, thrust upwards to meet her long curving pink tongue. Eventually the fawn tried to rise on stick-like legs, only to tumble back on to its haunches. After an hour the fawn was on its feet and nuzzling into the back legs of its dam, along her belly and even at her nose as she turned to lick its ears. It found the teats and pushed at them hard, sucked for perhaps half a minute before falling down, head dropping immediately into sleep.

Until recently many people believed that the roe deer of Sussex were descended from the last remaining wild indigenous stock of England, an ancient stock that roamed Roman Britain with the wolf and the boar. The remnants of this stock are supposed to have been protected within the walls of nearby Petworth Park. Whatever the true story is, certainly roe escaped from Petworth at the beginning of the twentieth century when the wall was breached by a tree torn down in a gale, and were then seen in considerable numbers in the woods around. Roe are found westwards in the New Forest, though it was only in 1880 that the former Royal Forest was repopulated with roe which came from Dorset. To the north, it is likely that roe in the Petersfield district were derived from the Surrey stock, again probably originating from the Petworth escapees.

Roe populations are notoriously difficult to determine. A density of 60–65 per 250 acres was found in Denmark after a wood was completely shot out (J. Andersen, 1953). On this basis there would be 90 roe deer in Kingley Vale, or one every 4 acres. Careful examination of rutting territories, of individuals, and of field marks, shows a steady increase from 3 pairs in 1964 to 6 pairs in 1977. They mainly frequent the eastern flanks of the escarpment where there is less human activity, and the scrub is dense enough and not thinned out by fallow deer. I expect to see an increase of roe into scrub areas as yet untrodden by deer. The main territory of the valley, however, is still occupied each year by the stand

ROE DEER

buck and his doe, even though this is also a favourite place of fallow.

What impact do roe have on the reserve? The browsing is less obvious than that of the fallow, which have brought all yews of less than 52 inches under their muzzles. Roe undoubtedly strip small yews in the hawthorn nurse area; this is not too worrying to the general dynamics of the yew forest but should, rather, be regarded as a natural phenomenon to be observed and annotated. A wave of regeneration of yew may well follow a relaxation in browsing pressure at some future time – either intentional or accidental, depending on how urgent the situation becomes. At the present it is not urgent.

Roe bucks are also guilty of thrashing the junipers, especially the smaller shrubs. With roe it is often a matter of luck as to how much thrashing is carried out at any particular place. A small territory edged the juniper bushes. The resident buck had made several fraying stocks on a variety of shrubs, one of them juniper. On these he had, as is usual with all bucks, left his scent. The scent is deposited by a gland in the head as the buck rubs it against the stock, and is his personal advertisement to other bucks to stay away. He will revisit the stocks at dawn and dusk, and often in the daytime too, near the rut. Usually a buck will scrape a shallow depression at the foot of the stocks and urinate in it, thus adding a little to the warning notice. He will also leave a certain amount of scent from glands on the back legs and back feet as he walks around. Now a questing buck, that is, one with not too fine a territory or whose doe has perhaps been temporarily commandeered by a stronger buck, will stumble on these stocks if he hasn't already smelt them downwind. It is said that he can judge sometimes by the smell if the resident buck is bigger than he is or not, and will act accordingly.

I have watched these questing bucks skirting territory that does not belong to them, and being very cautious about it too. Smaller bucks creep quietly, staring fearfully over the boundaries, hesitating, turning back; the bigger bucks will come boldly on. If the resident buck sees the visitor he will display. This is exactly what had happened among the juniper bushes one morning in July, though I did not see the action. The quester, I suspected, would have been about equal to the resident, both being three-year-olds. There were two sets of slots and two centres of activity, one of them against three of the prized junipers among other shrubs like yews and a hawthorn, and an adjacent activity against a small group of young yews. The junipers had been beaten down to mere stumps, with a metre of stem broken off in each bush. Thus it is the wandering bucks which cause the mischief by provoking the residents. By the end of the rut – usually the second week of August –

the activity is largely finished, except for small questing bucks that may make a nuisance of themselves among the does, though they too tend to 'vanish' with the bucks for a period of recuperation.

The resting bucks lie up sometimes within only 30 yards of the ring run, but most people never see them. One August the valley buck couched under a group of four or five yews, next to his rutting stand. I spent three days recording plants on the annual transect which crosses this stand. It was extremely hot, and each day I took shelter from the afternoon sun while having a drink. The buck, a six-year-old, sat in gloomy shade some 30 yards away, and appeared to be uninterested in my activities. Admittedly, I could only just see him, so well was I screened, but through binoculars I could see his antlered head resting on the ground, or held fairly low. In the evening he was not to be seen for the first two days. On the third I did see him standing up and feeding a little on yew leaves on the outside of his 'bedroom', but I only saw him because I knew where to look.

Autumn for roe deer usually means loafing around the old territories or summering grounds. In October some animals appear to begin rutting all over again. This is called the false rut, but on Kingley Vale it is very little in evidence. A little fraying here and there at the old stocks, a bit of excitement on the first few days of St Luke's Little Summer, a few wild-eyed roe running about in the ring runs, then it is over and the November rains quickly wash away the fun.

By winter, if it is a very frosty December with sleet and snow, the roe may gather into the sheltered valley bottom, travelling off the slopes of the reserve that face north and east and down into this south-facing bowl, usually keeping to family groups. In February and March they will graze in meadows and grassy glades until the bramble begins to grow in late March. At times quantities of rose and privet leaves are eaten. Young are born out in the open in the middle of the territories. Although they are mobile from birth, in practice they tend to lie still and depend on camouflage for their safety. This is often a useless defence against the large numbers of dogs which are allowed to roam as previously discussed, and two kids are known to have been killed on the reserve. One was only three days of age, born in the valley territory in 1975. A piteous screaming bleat like that of a wounded hare was heard close by the main track, and a Labrador dog was found retrieving the kid for its owner. Although apparently unharmed the wretched kid died within a minute, presumably from shock.

To sum up then, there are good and bad effects of such a large deer population: bad in that regeneration of the yew woodland is inhibited for the time being, though it must undoubtedly have been through such phases frequently in the past and survived. I think we need not worry about this – after all, one yew tree may occupy 10 square yards of ground and it could remain there for 500 years. Thus only once in 500 years does a tree need to be successful at that point. There has been a severe inroad into the juniper community, though the shrub is now known not to be so critical to the yew forest as was formerly thought. A purely mechanical means of defence should be sought to protect it rather than drastically limiting the numbers of deer present. The good effects are becoming more obvious month by month. The bramble collars spreading from around every 'island' clump of trees, covering many square yards of turf each year, as well as the spread of ash trees in glades, have been halted, and even reversed. Rank areas of grassland in small glades, dominated by tall species like cocksfoot and upright brome, are being returned to the diverse species-rich sward by the local grazing of deer. In short, at the present time there is emerging the kind of open, wild parkland, with its vistas and glades of short grazed turf, its woodland contours smoothed back by browse lines, which is not only a delight to look at but is as rich botanically and zoologically as it can possibly be – as the following chapters on birds, butterflies and plants will show. How long this can be allowed to last is a question that will one day have to be answered.

Hare

Kingley Vale is an ideal habitat for hares: in winter they lie up in the woodland – not the dense cover favoured by the rabbits, but the open, draughty spaces beneath the yews. The hares like to have a clear view around them, for their defence is in their phenomenal sprinting ability; they do not hide underground or in bramble bushes. But although with their side-set eyes they can see behind, they do like to have a fallen tree branch or a trunk, a low-hanging branch or even a big flint behind their backs. Then they will lie in their forms, which are no more than boat-shaped trodden pads of ground, watching all around them. One may walk by and never see them on an open field where they exactly match the dried-out brown turfs of old grassland, cultivated for arable. But in yew woodland their reddish-yellow winter coats are less camouflaged. Most people, being unobservant, will walk by a hare in its woodland form because there is much else to direct the eye – a patch of sunlight, strewn flints or chalk lumps, a pale root or fallen branch. Into this

HARE

mosaic the hare fits, and in winter lies up all day until dusk. Wait quietly and immobile by the woodland edge and you will see them come out on their pads or well-worn tracks. They feed in the valley grassland, unless there is a frost or snow when they will resort to the woodlands; ivy, low hawthorn buds or even twigs, blackthorn buds and bark, oak twigs (if there are any left), bramble and yew are all browsed, and remember that the hare can reach up to well over three feet by standing on its hindlegs.

The reserve is used mainly as a dormitory by the hares. There are plenty of 'smeuses' or passing places through gateways and tracks which show the diamond-shaped footprints of hares in the mud where they have gone out in the dusk and returned in the dawn. This is mainly in the spring, summer and autumn months when there is something to eat on the fields. They return to the reserve to eat more carefully the food which they have collected overnight. This is a kind of chewing the cud. Watch a hare in its daytime form for any period of time when it thinks it is alone and you will see it turn round and lick at its anus. It is taking the large, soft and undigested pellets of food to chew over thoroughly. The hard droppings that you see lying on the ground are the second passings. Rabbits do the same, but usually out of sight and underground.

It is the does which have territories, and the bucks wander about. I would estimate there to be one doe to every 10 acres, increasing to every 5 acres in peak times. In the reserve you can see the does in their forms in January and February when the weather is wild. In one year when they were causing damage to crops they were shot in their forms in February, and out of 8 does taken, 7 were just developing embryos. No jacks were shot in this way for they were mostly out in the open fields fighting.

One guide to population levels is the abundance of hares in a 52-acre field adjoining the reserve boundary. Does and bucks will all come out to play in the spring. On warm, calm evenings in April, when the majority of the rutting occurs, the hares leave the reserve and draw on to this particular field. The highest count I ever made was on 26 March 1972, when 42 hares were present at dusk; on 21 April 66 hares were scattered over four fields comprising about 100 acres, and most of these were thought to have come from the reserve. This would give a very rough winter population in the reserve valley (during December to February, when no hares were to be seen on the fields) of one hare to 3 acres. Normally the 52-acre field yielded a range of between 5 and 12 hares for all the years between 1964 and 1977. In 1969–70 and again in 1974–5 there were very low counts of only 3 hares. As the fields have always been either ley or cereals, counting is easy in March to April.

This annual congregation of hares is one of the most spectacular sights for the visitor, and it is a sad fact that few people seem to notice them even when they are displaying. By standing near the reserve's south-east corner, the smooth falling curve of the main (52-acre) field can be seen in profile. Much of what stands upon it – clod, flint, pheasant or hare – is in black silhouette against a greenish April sky. Groups of hares 'stand' around, upright on their haunches, holding their forepaws off the ground. With ears erect they can hear the slightest sound half a mile off. The does amble about the field, aware of the bucks but apparently not so, stopping to feed or smell a patch of ground. The bucks (and there may be four attendant on one doe) follow her whichever way she goes. She turns to the left so they follow left, like carriages behind a railway engine. She decides to run right or even about turn and go back; they want to go that way too. Never hurrying or trying to catch her or each other, they keep their distance, about a length, one from another. They make a maze of their courtship out on the chalky field.

Sometimes you may be lucky enough to see a boxing match between bucks. It does not occur often. Bucks will stand up facing one another and strike with very rapid blows. When they score, either on the pad of the rival or on his head, the sound is like someone smacking a small strap across a gloved hand. You have to be fairly close to hear this. Once I saw a buck with a piece out of the side of its ear as big as a new penny piece, and I have heard that they can blind one another too. Often fur flies, and you can find this lying about on the field. A kick delivered from the hind feet is another weapon: I once saw this delivered to a doe in company with a shower of stones and dirt. What the purpose was I do not know – it could have been jealousy for another doe.

Any of the convoy of a running group of hares may all at once behave as if it has come across hot ground. It may leap three yards to one side, twitching as if covered with fleas and shaking its forepaws as if they had dew on them. It may feed for several minutes, then kick out violently and run in a circle, frequently leaping sideways. This sideways leap is the usual method of losing a pursuer which is following scent. I have measured one such leap of four yards followed by a regular three-yard stride.

Each doe may breed four times per year. After 43 days of pregnancy, twins, triplets or quadruplets are born – the latter being more likely towards summer. The nursery of the woodland-born leverets is the mixed ash and yew wood, where a doe can hide her young under fallen trees. These woodland leverets are often taken by stoats, weasels, foxes and wandering dogs. I have seen at different times on the reserve a collie

64

dog, a mongrel and a Jack Russell snap up leverets and half eat them.

I have watched a stoat stalk one. The leveret was about two weeks old and lying in its form among deep moss on the slopes of the ash wood. The stoat knew exactly where its victim was, for it ran up close to it before starting an absurd dance, somersaulting and rolling about on the ground. This went on for some minutes. All at once it sprang on the leveret which emitted a pitiful scream. I was on the point of intervening, my perhaps unwarrantable protective instincts coming to the fore, when an old hare dashed through the wood, ran up to the stoat and appeared to leap across it, kicking it with her hindlegs as she passed over its back. The stoat rolled a little way and sprang to its feet, standing on hindlegs and making a yinnying noise of fear. The hare approached it making low muttering sounds, stamping her back legs on the moss. The two argued over the unfortunate leveret as it screamed thinly, then the hare rushed her opponent with flicking forelegs, and the stoat ran off and hid in an old rabbit burrow, continuing the spitting, vehement sounds. The doe stood near her young, staring at the stoat which then circled the pair at a wide distance, finally vanishing from view. Now she attended to the leveret, sniffing it over and licking its back once or twice, but constantly on the alert. Finally she crept off through the stems of dog's mercury. I went to look at the leveret, which had the usual punctures behind the head. I did not touch it, for it was still alive. The next day it had gone – either it was eaten or the doe had moved it.

Rabbit

Rabbits alone have had probably the greatest single effect on the reserve in the past 400 years. Aerial photographs taken before the 1940s show clearly the extent of rabbit distribution and give an idea of their abundance. The great armies of conies had dug themselves deep galleries into the chalk and flung out masses of material which showed as wide white patches from the air. Practically all of the head of the gulley was white, as were the western slopes. The chalk was exposed also by lack of any vegetation near the warrens. This showed up most clearly where the topsoil is thin, as on all the slopes. Photographs of some warrens in Sussex on flat ground, pre-myxomatosis, show a completely denuded soil with not even moss or lichens apparent over an area of about an acre.

The old description of 'carpets' of moving rabbits is not an exaggeration. In Wiltshire, in 1953, I remember seeing rabbits moving back into their warrens at my approach one evening: about an acre of land appeared to be on the move as the rabbits headed towards their burrows.

Similar descriptions are available for Kingley Vale. Mr Steve Pratt of Lavant vividly recalls an occasion when, as a boy, he witnessed an example of swarming rabbits.

We were up on Bow Hill about seven o'clock on a summer evening, just after the war. There were a few bushes then on the hilltop – otherwise turf and flints and quite open. All of a sudden we heard a rumbling noise. We couldn't think what it was, maybe a car or a truck rumbling over the stones. Then over the brow came a herd of rabbits. I should estimate the herd was 10–15 feet wide and 20–30 yards long. They were tightly packed together. They parted to avoid us and passed either side, then joined up again. There must have been hundreds and they just galloped on out of sight. I think they were moving to their feeding grounds, for the area around the warrens was bare.

When myxomatosis struck in 1953 there was widespread destruction in the reserve. In 1959, six years after the outbreak of disease, Dr A. S. Thomas commented that 'rabbits are now quite common again in Kingley Vale'. But myxomatosis reappeared frequently. From 1964 onwards I noticed dead rabbits almost every autumn. There was a particularly large outbreak in 1971 when a corpse was noted in every square 100 yards, in grassland, so that roughly 30–40 dead were found in the main valley from October to December. Dr Tittensor *et al.* have reported a 'slow increase' in rabbits on Bow Hill since M.A.F.F. research into population numbers began in 1971, despite the annual autumn outbreak of myxomatosis.

I have watched scores of rabbits in the last stages of the disease. This is the time when they will show themselves openly and unwittingly to view. They are blind and do not realise that they are visible. Quietly they creep along paths and tracks in daylight, and if one keeps still and downwind it is possible to have them pass within a few inches. Frequently stopping to touch their noses on the ground, they will attempt to find familiar scents and trails. If they suspect danger they have only their ears to help them locate it, and when they are alarmed they will gallop off blindly, often crashing headlong into obstructions.

It is now known that many rabbits become immune to the disease or recover from the infection – the latter can be identified by white 'scars' in the fur over the eyes. They are usually fully grown and appear in good

RABBIT

health. Young can be given immunity by the doe, for about six weeks after birth. Dr Tittensor and his colleagues found that 'a small number of apparently immune rabbits have subsequently shown symptoms of myxomatosis in the field'. But in another paper he says that 'Although immunity levels in the adult population were relatively high, a number of cases of apparent breakdown in immunity were discovered, possibly adding up to 10% of the rabbits catching the disease.'

Nowadays about one in four of the old burrows is occupied, but this is only a guide to population level. Another guide is provided by shooting bags. Mr Bob Warner of West Dean Estate has shot rabbits by headlight as they come out to graze on a field next to the 121-acre reserve of Bow Hill to the north-east of Kingley Vale. His annual bag used to be 800, but since 1972 when, as part of the legal requirements to control rabbits, we fenced our reserve boundary with netting, his annual totals have dropped to 400. Since only half of this part of the reserve produced any rabbits, a shootable surplus of 400 per 50 acres suggests 800 animals at least, or 16 to the acre.

Rabbits are probably one of the few wild animals that will be seen by the casual visitor to Kingley Vale. Young babies may sometimes be glimpsed playing outside in the sunlight, a few inches from the hole. 'Milky' does may be seen out in daylight, seeking the extra fodder required to keep up their milk supplies. Old bucks may come out in daylight too, to display by digging little holes and urinating in them, just like roe bucks.

When buck rabbits come out at dusk, it is not to feed but to fight and display. One April evening two bucks were so engrossed in fighting that they ran into my legs, then, rolling over in surprise, crashed into my dog who was sitting next to me. Nor did this encounter put them off, for they continued fighting within a minute. Favourite display points of dominant bucks have always been the ant-heaps which are scattered throughout Kingley Vale's pasture. Here they sit, perched well above the crowd (if there is one), surveying one another and the does which may be in the vicinity. Forty or fifty faecal pellets may be deposited on a favourite ant-heap in the course of 24 hours, and the enriched grass thereon either becomes blue-green with nitrogen and phosphate or dies for a time. Such a heap recorded in 1954 was still, in 1977, used for display by a descendant.

Fox

The common fox must be one of our better-known British mammals, if only for the controversy that surrounds certain human activities connected with him. For many years Kingley Vale was the traditional earth for a hunted fox. 'We'd always lose them in there', I was told when I came to the reserve. 'No matter how far they ran, if we were in that area they would make for it. I think they went up inside hollow yew trees.' And they could have done so, too: several large trees have holes into the centres through the bottom. A fox could easily climb up inside and be safe, just as squirrels will when hard-pressed.

Foxhunting is generally on the decline (though not in its traditional strongholds) for economic reasons and because countryside with open stretches of marginal land devoid of barbed wire at the disposal of forty galloping horses is at a premium, and also because fewer 'yeomen' farmers take part. Public opinion may have something to do with it: personally I have no time for the anti-foxhunting lobby, which I see as a social rather than a conservation argument.

When the woods near the reserve were taken in hand by an expert keeper in order to rear 3000 pheasants annually within their 200 acres, foxes had to be kept out. For nearly ten years the keeper snared 40 foxes per annum, and this number showed no signs of declining although there were adequate attractions in all other directions and many of his neighbours 'wired' too. Since he stopped snaring in 1975 the fox has become far more numerous in the reserve. (Curiously, the rabbit also has increased – but of course without the fox it might have increased even more.) The fox population consists of three main territories with cubs in each and some unmated adults. The 6–10 adults plus 15 cubs equals 20 or more foxes by early summer. Natural dispersal will ensure that this number is reduced by half by the following winter.

What is a fox's place on a nature reserve? There is no simple answer, because it depends on the complexities of a particular reserve's management and its neighbouring environment. Because the fox is so common, one can afford to manipulate its numbers locally. If, for example, a reserve has a nationally scarce species such as a little tern, foxes can be leaned on very heavily. It is no use allowing a little tern to go through the hoop half a dozen times – facing adverse migration weather, being captured for food in West Africa, having its eggs collected by oologists, its breeding beaches trampled and covered in oil slicks – and ending up with a thousand pairs in the whole of the British Isles, then to make it face another hoop – the fox – just for the sake of having a representative selection of British fauna on one's minute patch of land. It is only where two scarce creatures compete (for example little tern versus short-eared owl) that they should be left alone. Again, if one harbours foxes when all one's neighbours are trying to control them, one will become very unpopular, and for no good reason as the species is not endangered. The farming community may well think that the reserve is no better than a haven for vermin. So we try to co-operate as far as possible with the rest of the community, carrying out some fox control but only by humane methods such as shooting.

FOX

The fox undoubtedly takes a great deal of game (pheasants, partridge and probably young deer). An earth examined in March 1977 near the reserve contained nine dead pheasants, most of them cock birds. Another, five miles north-east, contained a cache of dead mice. In 1976 two earths on the reserve were conspicuous by the amount of pheasant and pigeon feathers, hare and rabbit bones and fur scattered around in the cubs' play area.

Anyone wanting to see cubs at play may be lucky if they sit at dusk opposite and downwind of one of these playgrounds, in April to June. Cubs come above ground as early as the end of March, particularly if the vixen is disturbed – on 23 March 1976 I watched a procession of six cubs following the vixen like puppies as they moved from one side of the reserve to the other in the evening. Normally the first warm days of April see the cubs out playing regularly. As they await the return of the vixen who is off foraging, they fight each other, rolling over in the dry hollows scraped out of old ant-hills, biting and growling over rabbit feet, leg bones or pheasant feathers, and all the while watching out for danger. When the vixen returns, perhaps carrying a mouse, a rabbit or a bird, they will rush to her and either grab her offering or, if they are young enough, butt her teats like young lambs. Such moments may be rare even for a warden, for he does not, after all, have a great deal of spare time for sitting down on his reserve. But one April day in 1977 I had a rare and unexpected sight which was something of a bonus in the day's work.

It was not until I saw the vixen carrying home a young rabbit through the dew that I knew there was a litter of foxcubs under my very nose. I know the hill slope well, and had not seen much trace of a fox just there. But here she was, this young mother with her first brood of cubs, looking slim despite a line of teats along her belly. The rabbit was held by the neck, and she kept her head high as it swung against her chest. She was as red as the sun that was rising through the mist, her legs slim and edged with black and some grey. She was only 20 yards from me as she slipped like a cat through the wire fence. Then she went to the side, and there was a lot of whimpering and scuffling and puppy-like growling, and to my astonishment I realised that I was sitting next to her earth. Luckily my dog was not with me, or even worse, a human companion. I thought how many of my gamekeeper friends would like to be there with a gun, but this moment was between me and the vixen.

Listening for foxes in late December to early January gives some idea too of population numbers. They begin calling on frosty starlit nights at around 6 p.m. After some careful watching of the paths and tracks through the wood as I go about my daily business, I have managed to see something of these nocturnal travellers. Their pad-marks give them away, for a fox's trail is completely different to that of a dog. The foot is narrower, with small toes and sharp claw-marks, and the pad imprint is partly masked by the furriness of the foot. I had seen these prints much in evidence on a certain muddy path through the yew trees. Happening to be about at crack of dawn in this part of the wood, I saw a big old white-tipped dog trotting for home, with his head down and his brush held low. He had not the slightest clue that I was about, so I gave him a rabbit squeal by sucking the back of my hand and he turned round as though shot and stared at me full face for a minute. He did not like it though, so he ran on, I suspect to an earth inside a big old hollow yew, frequented by out-lying foxes for many years. Perhaps his mind was on better things than food, for the next day in that spot, towards dusk, I saw another fox – a very small vixen, probably a last year's cub now grown up and already thinking about cubs of her own.

Badger

Many of the people who come to Kingley Vale ask if there is any possibility of seeing a badger. Television has helped to make familiar the white head with its conspicuous black stripes on either side, and although many thousands of people now know what the badger looks like, they are certainly not aware of the time and patience involved if they are really to see one in the wild. The hours of sitting still, preferably up a tree (an uncomfortable perch) to cut to a minimum any chance of disturbing the badger's routine with human scent, is beyond the powers of the average human. They must move, cough, sigh, and then wonder why they never see anything!

The most notable feature about the badger, apart from its striped face and strong jaws, is its very powerful legs, developed for digging. Each foot has five toes (dogs and foxes have four), with particularly large claws on the front feet.

Badgers live in 'setts' under ground, and in well-established setts the series of underground passages and chambers can be very complex. There is always more than one entrance and there may be several different levels, the whole being like some ancient underground castle. The chambers are lined with bedding, and much activity is devoted to collecting bracken and grass for this purpose; stale bedding is removed periodically and carted some distance away. Further evidence of the badgers' cleanliness is the latrine pits which are dug some distance from the sett.

During the winter months badgers are quiescent, but there is no true hibernation and they often forage for food in cold weather. However, they may stay underground for days at a time, living on the fat stored under their skins. They have well-developed musk glands which give off an extremely strong smell. This is used for territory marking and also in excitement and fear. Badgers mate in early spring (February to May) but implantation is delayed until about the following December. The young are usually born in February, two or three to a litter.

There are three old badger setts on the reserve, last occupied in 1976, 1973 and 1968 respectively. The cause of the badger's disappearance is not entirely clear. I have observed on several occasions how increased human access to land scares them away from well-established setts, but in our case the less disturbed setts were vacated first. The smallish sett of four to five holes in a sand pocket in Cp. 13 was first, followed by a very deep excavation in chalk in Cp. 19; lastly, the biggest of the three at the bottom of the coombe in Cp. 10 was vacated. It is quite possible that disturbance by fox-seeking terriers and their owners caused the badgers to move on.

The Sussex Mammal Report of 1970–71 states:

> Records of badgers indicate a similar pattern of abundance in Sussex over the past decade, and while a number of setts have undoubtedly been lost to building development there is no evidence of a general decline. There are large numbers of setts in use, particularly in the east of the county which seems to have a genuinely higher population of badgers than the west.

Mr E. D. Clements conducted a survey of Sussex badgers in a national scheme run by the Mammal Society in 1971–2. He found well over 1000 setts in Sussex, with more areas still to be searched. In the general area of the reserve, the four square miles surrounding and including Kingley Vale held only between 3 and 12 setts (3 of these being on the reserve). The whole of West Sussex held well under 100 setts compared to nearly 1000 for East Sussex. This is an extremely curious situation since East Sussex is generally less wooded, particularly along its downland ridge, and therefore the badger should be more accessible to its human enemies. Mr Clements notes: 'Prolonged periods of severe control measures by keepers have considerably reduced the numbers of badgers in the Worthing – Chichester – Haslemere area'. In my experience, keepers do not talk openly about destroying badgers. They know it to be unpopular.

Although some protection was given by the Protection of Badgers Act, 1973 (for example, making gassing illegal), keepers are still able to destroy badgers with the approval of the owners of the land if the animals are known to be doing damage. I know that considerable snaring of badgers was carried out by certain keepers and still is, in 1977.

Badgers have a varied diet, as is shown by their droppings. Pulpy soft droppings are most likely to indicate a diet of earthworms. George Barker (Assistant Regional Officer, N.C.C.) studied the diet of badgers at Old Winchester Hill National Nature Reserve, nearby in Hampshire. He thought that 90 per cent of their diet was earthworms. I lived for a time near this reserve, and once or twice little parcels arrived addressed to 'The Warden', to be opened with puzzled anticipation by myself or my wife. They contained evil-smelling badger droppings which had to be hurriedly posted on before they exploded. Badgers from Kingley Vale would trespass into wheat and barley (a large amount of chalk is passed too when they harvest grain); they would dig out wasps' nests frequently, and dig down through the top of a rabbit's stop for the young, thus saving themselves the labour of digging out the whole tunnel. Barker found faeces composed entirely of crane flies' remains. As well as eating large numbers of yew arils, they are known to lick up hawthorn berries and even nuts in winter. Blackberries, the occasional slow worm, and picnic remains (chewed butter papers and metal cupcake containers give this away) complete a fairly harmless diet. Clements notes that badgers do little damage agriculturally, although they may occasionally take chickens. Cereals in the vicinity of a sett are often flattened and some may be eaten, but only a very small percentage of the total crop is affected.

In the late 1960s the then Nature Conservancy investigated the deaths of 17 badgers in south-eastern England, showing that the livers of at least 8 contained dieldrin, 5 contained DDT and/or its derivatives and 3 contained heptachlor epoxide. Five of the 17 were genuine road deaths, but of the remainder 6 certainly and 6 more very probably died of dieldrin poisoning. During 1970–71 58 badger road deaths were reported in Sussex (*Sussex Mammal Report*, 1970–71). In East Sussex three badgers, young and adults, were found dead well away from roads, in woods or on open downland, with several others near to setts. One body was buried but later found disinterred 10 feet away. This brings to mind a story told to me one day by a visitor to the reserve.

This lady, a keen naturalist, was walking at dusk through the wood when she heard the screams of a vixen. She stood still and listened, and after ten minutes they gradually ceased. By now it was fairly dark, but she found her way through the undergrowth with the aid of a pocket torch, and there found a dead vixen. There appeared to be no sign of wounds or broken bones but the fur of the neck was ruffled. Extremely puzzled, she made a thorough examination and found the spoor of badger in the soft earth. She then buried the corpse in a shallow grave and on returning the next day to have a closer look found that it had been dug up, the footprints of a badger again covering the soft ground. What is strange about this was that she had experienced the same incident at that spot six years before.

Badgers do not like the company of foxes, presumably because of the scent, although it is known for the two to inhabit the same earth (or should one say sett?), in which case there would be more than one entrance. Badgers have their young usually in February, foxes a little later, and I think that the above story was a case of two females fighting over the only breeding chambers available.

On another occasion one night in spring a friend, an experienced observer of wildlife, was watching a fox earth that was situated near a badger sett. Both vixen and badger sow had cubs. Noticing that the foxcubs playing outside had become extremely agitated, she was amazed to see the boar emerge from the fox earth with the vixen in his mouth. The vixen was kicking wildly, but to no avail, and the badger disappeared with her down a backdoor entrance to his own sett, presumably to dispose of the remains.

Stoat and Weasel

The fortunes of stoats may well be linked with those of the rabbit. In Sussex generally, an increase of stoats has been reported since the late 1960s. *The Sussex Mammal Report* for 1969 recorded 'a remarkable resurgence and this may not yet have reached the peak of the cycle', though two years later 'a slight increase in stoat numbers, though a few observers reported a local scarcity' suggested that the peak had been reached. In the reserve, sightings increased with the general resurgence of rabbits until today (1977) it is possible to see, on one watchful walk through the Vale, three or four stoats.

The territory of a male is suggested as being approximately 50 acres (Southern, *Handbook of British Mammals*, 1964), with areas within this territory being used successively for a few days; an animal may

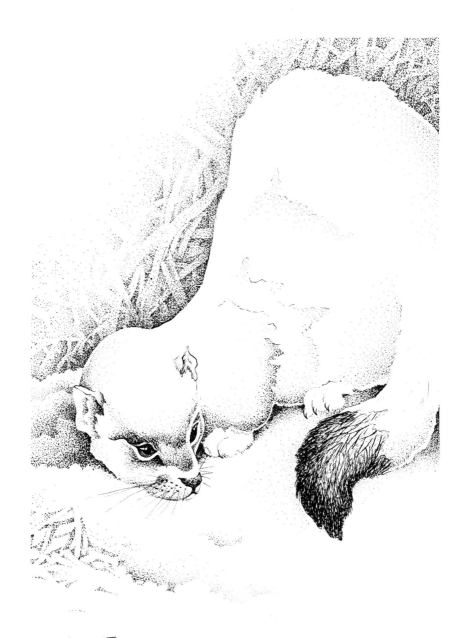

ERMINE

travel up to five miles in one night as it hunts through its area. The stoat 'castles' have always been found in the old deep warrens burrowed out of coombe rock deposits in Cp. 8 and 9 in the valley. The tell-tale 'necklaces' of rabbit or mouse fur give away these underground haunts. The droppings may be as long as 4 inches, and ten or more can often be counted lying near to the entrances of the rabbit burrows, sometimes being deposited within an area on a small knoll. Such a large number of fresh droppings indicates that a family is in residence, as I discovered to my surprise on Blakeney Point in June 1963 when common terns were being taken on the nest. On that occasion fourteen stoats were trapped in one night from about four rabbit burrows, several traps being used outside each burrow at once.

The stoat is almost certainly very destructive to woodland birds. Can it be tolerated on a reserve? In the case of a reserve where the main interest is not birds, and where no really rare or threatened birds breed, the answer is obviously yes, it can, as an interesting member of Britain's natural fauna. I have seen stoats (and weasels) climbing rapidly up into the tops of large yew trees, so they are able to predate almost all woodland birds. A stoat was described by Michael Boxall, our Honorary Warden, 'running about in the branches and crown of an oak after climbing the trunk like a squirrel' in May 1977. It then jumped into a yew and finally descended from its tree hunt via a sloping ash trunk. It was obviously bird-nesting. Local gamekeepers think I am daft not to shoot them on sight.

Whenever I see a stoat hunting I call it to me by imitating a rabbit's squeal. This sound, caused by sucking air between the lips and the back of the hand, is usually irresistible to a stoat, provided one is downwind. The stoat may disappear from view, to reappear beside one within a few seconds having travelled through dense bushes with the ease of water through a sieve. There it will stand on hindlegs, fear battling with curiosity as it runs closer, backs off, all the while trying to focus on the source of the squeals with black-bead eyes. I have often watched a stoat hunting its prey, though one incident in particular sticks in my mind.

It was obvious which rabbit was going to die. Not only did I, a hundred yards away and watching through my telescope know, but the rabbit, one of a dozen sitting outside in the morning air, knew as well. Death was a long way off still, but the rabbit saw it coming and just sat down and gave up. Its squeals were pitiful to me, yet I did nothing to help, knowing that to intervene in a natural event was pointless and sentimental. The stoat rippled like a piece of brown silk through the grass dozens of yards behind. Other rabbits there were to right and left, a hundred intersecting scents where they had gambolled and fed, but the stoat stayed fixed on the one of its choice.

As the stoat came nearer, and obviously not being very hungry, it played near to its wretched victim, tumbling about and somersaulting, falling down and rolling about, a trick more usually employed to entice rabbits close out of curiosity. Many of the rabbits there drew a little nearer to their old enemy, including one large doe. She, however, was not to be fooled by the dance, and as the victim continued its pathetic screams she rushed at the stoat, turned her back and gave it a powerful kick. Perhaps the young rabbit was her own offspring. The stoat raised itself on its hindlegs and swore horribly, a kind of hissing 'yah, yah' that went on for ten minutes or more, while the doe turned and again kicked out savagely. She so confused the hunter that eventually it went off in the wrong direction, and as the sun came over the hill every rabbit, including the by now lucky one, went below ground.

On another occasion I was puzzled by the sight of a stoat carrying something in its mouth as it galloped along the path towards me. Was it a small rat or a mouse, or perhaps a newborn and naked rabbit that it was taking to its brood? But I was not to see, at least not for a while, because unfortunately my dog was twenty yards ahead of me on the path and the stoat saw her first. It stopped abruptly, raised itself and the load on to its hindlegs, and stared. While I was fumbling for binoculars the stoat vanished, and I cursed the missed opportunity. Still staring along the path my eye caught a glimpse of a brown flash to the side. There was the stoat, racing through the long grass and the bramble bushes as though they did not exist. Imagining the young about to enjoy their meal, I was rather taken aback when, a few seconds later, the stoat appeared on the path again, this time coming in the opposite direction.

There was momentary fear that this determined little animal, not a foot in length and with stubby legs a couple of inches long, was not this time going to deviate. I remembered how my grandfather was once climbed over by a family of stoats as he stood in their path, though he was not in fact hurt by them in any way. But it passed close by me again at a gallop and vanished far ahead along the path. Within three minutes it was back again with its burden. This time I was ready, and dog and I stepped aside and watched the mother go by. Yes, that was her role: she had one of her babes in her mouth, gripped by the scruff of the neck, and its feet were curled up to avoid hitting the ground. Seven times the bitch stoat went by on that path at intervals of exactly seven minutes. She must have travelled 600 yards on each trip, until all the brood were safely installed in a new burrow.

But that was not the end of the encounter. Having watched the burrow for some days during my travels, I found the family once more on the move, this time under their own steam. They were considerably bigger than the week before, but very young still, and so mindful of their mother that she had somehow got them to hold each other's tails in their mouths so as not to stray off the path. Mother led her brood through the grass until they disappeared like a sinuous brown snake. But I shall never know why they decided to move house twice in one week.

The stoat is sometimes seen in ermine. In 1977 a pure white animal lived from November until the end of March within half a mile of the Vale at Welldown Copse and the surrounding fields. At this time several brown-coated animals were seen too. There was another ermine in that same winter on Goodwood's Trundle, four miles away. But several years previously seven parti-coloured stoats were trapped at nearby Chilgrove, all within a week and at the same place. Although the skewbald animals were not all exactly the same pattern, they were alike enough to make me think they were of the same family.

The stoat's smaller cousin is the weasel. It has a shorter tail and the black tip, so prominent on the stoat's tail, is absent. Its teeth are sharp, pointed and powerful, and the neck and jaw muscles are very strong. One characteristic is the long flexible neck, which shows up when the weasel is alert and questing the air, a typical pose.

Although its diet is predominantly voles and mice, the weasel, too, is highly destructive to birds.

The Sussex Mammal Report for 1970–71 records:

There were several instances of tit nest-box occupants being predated by weasels, and in one case a sleeping weasel was disturbed in a nest-box previously occupied by six fledgling marsh tits. Near Bexhill one weasel was watched taking eggs from a bird's nest and later one was seen examining a nest five feet off the ground.

The stoat and the weasel have only one enemy in Kingley Vale. This is the subject of the next section.

Feral Cat

Feral cats, that is, domestic cats that have gone wild, turn up frequently in this reserve, as they do on many others. The warden of a Kentish woodland reserve shoots about a score every year. They nest in old squirrel dreys and have to be poked out. 'One day', this warden told me, 'I shook a hornbeam pole at the top of which was a drey, I suspected a cat had used it. Six half grown cats sprang out of it and shinned up to the top twigs and there clung, spitting at me. I shot the lot.'

Cats are well known for their ability to keep down mice and rats. Sometimes, a cat will stick to this diet exclusively. I have a cat at home like this. It is worth its weight in Warfarin. Were it to take to killing birds I should have no hesitation in dispatching it. Without the most time-consuming research into the activities of every feral cat, one cannot give them the benefit of the doubt. At some time, somewhere, one would come across a nightingale's nest; a willow warbler or song thrush would never be safe, even the only spotted flycatcher on the reserve, her nest bound by a few strands of moss to the side of a smooth ash trunk, would go, when the young were fit to take. All of these species are actual examples of plundered nests that I have known about. Other birds such as blackbird, mistle thrush, chiffchaff which have been predated were not necessarily the work of a cat, and may have been grey squirrel.

At one time five cats were known to live in the valley. There were four black-and-white animals and an old fluffy brown queen I called Brown Mog. Two of the piebald cats were shot, another was trapped in neighbouring woods. Many people saw Brown Mog stalking young rabbits or mice and described her as a fox, a puma or even an otter. One youngster said he had seen a 'long, short, wriggling sort of brown bear' which could only have been Brown Mog. Once I saw her killing a stoat. She started life as a large but slim thick-coated tortoiseshell, roaming the hills and the far eastern boundaries – once as far away as Goosehill Camp in Cp. 19. As the years went by she became heavier and her coat was a camouflage of earth and shadow pattern, matted with burs and bramble and the mud of deep rabbit warrens. In the last years she came to live permanently in the warm, south-facing valley.

Once I was sitting quietly on a fallen yew trunk having a sandwich, with my dog at my side, when she stiffened and stared behind me, her brow deeply furrowed with curiosity. I turned to see Brown Mog not ten yards away. She was as big as a vixen, with a bushy tail and pointed tufts to her ears. She stood on her dawn shadow which stretched towards us four or five yards and her eyes were like eclipsed suns. My dog leapt from the slip and there was a short chase. When I came to her she was staring up into one of the old pollard yews wagging her tail, ridge-backed with subsiding hair. Seeing me she leapt at the tree's smooth sides, falling back. Twice, three times she dashed herself at the trunk in frustration. Brown Mog could run *and* climb. But to where had she climbed? There

FERAL
CAT

was no sign of the branch tops swaying. I climbed up, the dog whimpering behind, searched every branch to its twig and foliage end, but found no cat cleverly concealed. Then I saw a hole in the trunk where the tree had amputated a limb. It was hollow! It was easy after that to notice the few hairs which adorned that entrance and the many other entrances to holes in trees throughout the valley. Brown Mog lived for ten years; she was killed by a fox or dog in the spring of 1976.

Other Mammals

Several other mammals live within the reserve, but their import upon the scientific interest is marginal. Hedgehogs are occasionally seen, large black slugs being at least one of their items of diet. They may well impinge on the ground-nesting birds (they certainly do eat terns' eggs).

The common brown rat is seen occasionally. Once I watched a family of youngsters, perhaps six weeks old, playing in the branches of a yew tree, their nursery. They climbed carefully and inquisitively along the polished and slippery limbs, with tails half grasping the bark, stopping frequently to look down. One morning I saw an old doe running on an urgent errand, holding a dead blackberry leaf in her mouth. She disappeared inside a bramble bush; parting the stems I saw a large mound of leaves like a football. At this moment my dog, who had once picked up and shaken a rat to death, was reminded of the joy of breaking bones and jumped head first into the bush, frightening out the rat and burying his teeth in the mound of leaves. He peeled off the first layer like the skin of an orange, followed by successive layers representing days of work put in by the rat to house her young. The middle of the nest was reached, and here the softest bramble leaves, the furry ones that feel like strips of calf suede, were laid circularly in a cavern no bigger than a cricket ball. Idle curiosity had overcome my will to protect the rat's labour, though I convinced myself that my inaction was justifiable for the purposes of scientific record.

Field vole and bank vole are recorded regularly. Now and then a dormouse is discovered in thick gorse bushes. One was still in hibernation in May one year although the temperature was 60° F. Harvest mice have been seen in long grassland a mile from the reserve, so they probably live within the boundaries too.

The most surprising find was a water shrew, a dead male found on the plateau in June 1976. Its slaty-black upper fur and silvery belly made it stand out some distance away, and as it was dead there was no mistaking the identification. The nearest water (apart from one concrete-sided fire pond of 10 yards square, one mile away) is the River Ems five miles away, although a small bourne nearly two miles away at Stoughton had been running some months previously. The Lavant had been dry for months. Woodland, but not heathland, is recorded as being a subsidiary habitat of this small mammal (*Handbook of British Mammals*).

Common and pygmy shrews are recorded. In the dry summer of 1976, several 'gangs' of excited common shrews were frequently seen rushing hither and thither among the rough grassland of the valley, as well as in local coppice woodland. Although the drought had hardened the ground, so that earthworms were virtually unobtainable for some months, this had not impaired their mating fervour. As their diet includes grasshoppers and spiders, this ensured that they survived the high summer drought, since parts of the valley grassland swarmed with grasshoppers in the summer of 1976, with estimates in areas of highest densities of up to 100 grasshoppers per square yard. The unfortunate mole, however, died off in some numbers and was almost not seen in the spring of 1977 although it had once been common in the grassland (especially in the areas of coombe rock deposits lying in the bottom of gulleys and under the yew trees on the slopes).

Of the introduced wild mammals, grey squirrels are by far the commonest though mink did exist just after the 1939–45 war when they were bred for fur at Blackbush (near Cp. 19). There are roughly two grey squirrel dreys per acre of old woodland. A population of two adults and four young would be the least that would be living in such a density, judging by the numbers of animals dislodged from dreys during clearance operations. Many of the dreys are used as secondary nests by does and communally by males (three males were dislodged from one in April 1977). Given 200 acres of suitable grey squirrel habitat, this would give at the least a midsummer population of 400 for the whole reserve. The grey squirrel is a particularly destructive animal. Not only does it rob birds' nests (mistle thrush nests nearly always seem to be plundered, particularly the first nests, when young have hatched, and at the Sussex Trust's reserve at Flatropers Wood squirrels damaged tit nesting-boxes) but it also damages some trees so badly that they are stunted and become prone to disease.

Beech trees all over the local estates have been so afflicted, including those grown next to the reserve since the war. At times, half the tree is girdled and the callouses that cover the wounds are again attacked in a later year. At Marden yew forest, owned by Mr David Gault, I saw yew trees of about 100 years of age stripped of bark all down one side from a height of 16 feet right down to the ground. Luckily the yews at Kingley Vale are not badly damaged, although areas of up to half a square yard have been stripped of bark on quite a few trees. The main damage they do is by twig cutting: particularly on old trees in the valley, squirrels clip leafy twigs off by the hundred to make their dreys in summer. They are particularly wasteful, leaving many twigs representing 3–4 years' growth lying around on the ground, and the trees consequently have a rather thin crown, like a May-frosted oak. The dreys, made of yew twigs and lined with the shredded bark of old man's beard or of green-cut leafy oak twigs, are the size of a medicine ball, tightly woven together. Three or four naked and blind young are born usually in March, and some more in summer. Now and then dead adults, sometimes with dead young, are found in the dreys. Though no post-mortems have been carried out it is possible that they have fed on organo-phosphorous dressed grains in neighbouring fields. Grey squirrels occasionally do some good. In the long drought of 1969 and 1976 they took to stripping sycamore bark in Cp. 19, killing the aerial shoots of scores of this foreign 'invader', thereby saving the warden a lot of work! (The sycamore deprives the system of more useful insect-supporting natives such as beech, oak or ash.) Other trees known to be barked in Sussex by squirrels are hornbeam, birch, silver birch, willow and Scots pine.

Squirrels are shot on sight in the reserve. I do not think, given the numbers of wandering dogs and visitors all through the year as well as the other wildlife, that we should consider using the more efficient Warfarin technique of killing squirrels. This involves storing poisoned wheat in special metal hoppers into which only squirrels are supposed to gain access. In fact numbers of mice are also able to take the food, and undoubtedly widespread deaths are caused. Although it is not known how dangerous the poison is to birds, there is cause for concern, and research is being undertaken to find out more.

Numbers of squirrels fluctuate, like any mammal population. In the *Sussex Mammal Report* for 1970–71, Mr P. S. Laurie of the Wartling Hill Grey Squirrel Club of Herstmonceux in Sussex gives figures for bag totals from 1949, a consistent method of destruction being used from year to year. This showed a grey squirrel peak in 1954 (curiously the year of myxomatosis) dropping rapidly away, and two much smaller peaks occurring in 1962 and 1970. Males outnumbered females in the ratio 100:82 (100:94 for nestlings) in all years except for 1954, 1968 and 1971 when the ratio was 100:141 (100:121 for nestlings).

Reptiles

Adders and common lizards are the only reptiles that I have seen on the reserve. Both are well scattered and not often seen, though the adder can turn up in more unusual places. Thus in April 1974 a large snake slid silently by my daughter who was sitting on the steps to the Field Museum. I had never seen a snake in this area before, nor have I seen one since. He was just questing and may have come some distance. Normally, adders are found in the central gulley around the old rabbit

ADDER

warrens, in which they undoubtedly hibernate, and on the plateau, particularly in the vicinity of the most north-eastern tumulus where they hibernate inside this great mound of flints.

Adders are found in surprising colours: lovely sky-blue males may be seen coiled with deep brick-red females in April. Once I saw a female give birth to a young one. She was coiled up with two little black babes when she began to heave, and from her abdomen a white papery case bulged and burst, a wriggling adder only four or five inches long falling on to the grass. She caressed them all with her forked tongue.

It is said that only six people in the last 250 years have been killed by adder bites in England. Others have had extremely unpleasant bites, as for example one lady I met on the reserve who had been bitten in the New Forest and whose leg was swollen to almost twice its proper size for a year. Therefore it is as well to be cautious when wandering off the proper paths into the long grass.

Snails

Twenty species of snail have been identified on the reserve (see Appendix). Of particular note are the huge numbers of banded snails in the chalk grassland. There are great numbers of brown-lipped snails too. On May Day one year I watched two of them making love. One was yellow with a sporty brown stripe running round its shell. The other had four brown stripes as if it were dressed in an Edwardian boating blazer. I bent down to watch, my knees getting soaked with dew. The two snails were on a grass stem, facing one another; they had grey rubbery lips with which they caressed one another delicately, then gently slid by each other, touching all the time. I looked for the firing of the tiny darts which snails employ to stimulate each other, but on this occasion was out of luck. (These chalk barbs are visible to the naked eye but not often seen.) They passed, then turned and came back again. It went on for five minutes, and I thought of John Clare's description of the snail 'with earnest heed and tremulous intent, frail brother of the morn . . .'

The Chalk Grassland

The Sward

After the yew forest, the next most important habitat of this reserve is chalk grassland. Chalk grassland is confined to downlands or chalk hills. It becomes more rare as areas are ploughed up, planted with trees or enriched with chemical fertilisers which encourage coarser species such as cocksfoot grass. On the South Downs its existence is due to a pure accident of economic history, because sheep were profitable and their close cropping encouraged the sward over hundreds of years. Areas that have not been completely destroyed but were merely reverting to woodland, are now becoming interesting once again due to grazing by rabbits and, lately, sheep. Thus great areas in Wiltshire, on Porton Down particularly, are once more becoming grazed back to their former condition. East Sussex too has a considerable area, still mainly on its north-facing downland slopes. There is a smaller area in West Sussex, since this is a much more wooded county, having a greater seed source to colonise the grassland slopes once grazing had ceased. Many land-owners actually planted their north-facing slopes with beech and conifers, but some that remain as chalk grassland are at Treyford, Didling and Bepton Down, about five miles from Kingley Vale, and at Harting Downs. These slopes are grazed, but only by cattle at the present time with consequent 'poaching' or opening-up of the turf cover in wet weather.

Thus the turf at Kingley Vale is not unique, by any means, and its area is very small in the national context, but it is the only turf in West Sussex at the present time that has any statutory protection, and it adds variety to the reserve which is useful educationally. The tricky question has already been asked: for how long are the beautiful glades of fine grassland to be held back as grazed or mown turf before being allowed to revert to woodland? At the moment, they are a most aesthetically pleasing foil to the sombre dark green yew forest, with bright green, almost emerald vistas and glades opening up in all directions, catching many shades of light and shadow. But however pleasing is the overall effect, it is nothing to the detail. Altering one's perception from the distant view of smoothly rounded downs, to the glades darting here and there throughout the valley, down to the view before one's feet of dozens of different species of grass and sedge and flowering herbs, then finally to the perfect miniature shapes of individual flowers – thyme and harebell, bellflower and rockrose – is like moving through a series of Alice looking-glasses, with each perspective more brilliant than the last.

W. H. Hudson in his *Nature in Downland* described the summertime scene:

> The vegetation has the appearance of a beautiful tapestry worked in various shades of green, roughened with the slender dry bents standing out like pale yellow thread-ends from the green texture; flecked, and in places splashed with brilliant colour – red, purple, blue and yellow. Or if you look at the flowers with the sun before you they appear like shining gems sewn into the fabric and forming an irregular pattern.

Hudson would have been able to walk for mile upon mile on the springy turf, in fact much of the way to Beachy Head, eighty odd miles away. The South Downs in those days must have been one of the best-known walking grounds in the country, as it is today.

The chalk turf of Kingley Vale is notable for its masses of hairy violets, which give the turf almost the same blue haze seen on other downs when rampions and scabious flowers are in bloom. It is probably one of the best places in the country to see the flower.

After the violets, the turf remains blue for the first part of the year. Late April sees the sky-blue flowers of bird's-eye speedwell, which being a coloniser carpets areas recently grazed by rabbits, verges of paths and newly mown grassland. In 1977 it formed dense blue carpets many yards square when gaps appeared in the grassland after the 1976 drought. Even earlier than this, the little early forget-me-not sends up thousands of one inch high flower spikes from the often bare tops of ant-heaps. After the drought it too colonised well, marking blue circles scattered mainly across the old horse-grazed turf where the horses had broken open the tops of some defunct ant-heaps; an unfortunate but luckily slight 'poaching' of the grasslands begun in the wet winter of 1974–5.

Other colonisers of the bared turf are the minute flowered thyme-leaved sandwort and the thyme-leaved speedwell. In April and May the pathways, not yet worn by thousands of trampling feet, show up their exact outlines by the masses of daisies – foaming white ribbons through the reserve. These 'white paths' remain for at least seven years after the trampling has ceased, then as the impacted soil begins to be broken up by frost and the action of worms the daisies gradually die out. Quantities of dandelions grow as well on these paths, four times as many as are found naturally in the turf.

A little while later the most delicate flower of the chalk is found – fairy flax, with thread-like stems and white flowers. Two species of thyme (*Thymus drucei* and *T. pulegioides*) form intricate and dense little mats across up to half a square yard of turf, often flowering down the sides of ant-hills and spreading out across the ground like some greeny-purple stage curtain. Closely related to the thymes is another aromatic herb, marjoram, often used in cooking particularly by the French. If you want some buy a 10p packet of seed from a shop and leave mine alone, because it is needed by the butterflies who swarm to its clusters of small dark purple flowers at the top of the dense stems which grow up to 2 feet high. Various patches grow year after year in the same spots, attracting large clouds of blues, brown argus and other insects. It is reputed to have given, along with thyme, the distinctive flavour to Southdown mutton, but I noted with interest that the sheep turned out into the reserve in 1977 would not touch it or the other aromatic herb wood sage, a plant beloved of moths and cooks. Perhaps the hardier Southdown breed were better adapted to the strong herbs of wild downland.

Other members of the thyme family are not so specialised. Thus wild basil, or cushion calamint, is an opportunist, unlike the faithful thyme, and will quickly fill in gaps created by cutting or over-grazing. Its downy soft, pale leaves are faintly reminiscent of its more stringent cousin, but it has the lax, loose habit of one that does not have to struggle for survival. Self-heal and betony, ground ivy and bugle are all members of the thyme family which grow here and there throughout the reserve, particularly ground ivy which straggles with purple trailing stems all over the valley grassland. Bugle is so beautiful that it reminds one of a bright blue orchid. It is one of the most loyal of plants, appearing time and time again in its few favourite haunts in damp soil. Another of the pungent thymes is the dead-nettle. The first of the white dead-nettles are usually to be seen on May Day, standing starkly white and staring in the dusk of the track-side on the approach to the reserve; but there are not many of these 'marginal ground' or 'waste ground' type of plants, typical of continually disturbed land, in the reserve, and I should be rather worried if they did appear in any number, except perhaps around the border of encroaching woodland – where the last of this distinctive family, the yellow archangel, has been seen recently here and there.

Another minute plant of the ant-hills is squinancy wort, which will sometimes dominate an entire ant-hill, its bright green leaves, arranged in whorls of four, and dense tiny white or pink flowers making a soft cushion in the turf. It is a member of the bedstraw family, which only becomes obvious when the arrangement of the leaves is noticed, the cross of leaves resembling crosswort and other bedstraws. Squinancy wort frequently grows in common with lady's bedstraw on ant-hills, and then a marvellous yellow and white mosaic can be seen which, when mixed with the mauve of thyme, is far prettier than any formally planted rock garden. Sometimes heath bedstraw grows with the lady's bedstraw, but more often it is found by itself on the more acid soils of the plateau, now and then close to patches of crosswort. The larger, more straggling hedge bedstraw often climbs like a web among old bramble stems and is carried aloft by rising grass stems in the coarser valley grassland.

Most of these plants are to be found in exactly the same place year after year. Research in Russia has shown that many plants of the chalk may have been in place for up to 200 years – a fact most clearly illustrated to me by the horseshoe vetch which always flowers, but never spreads, in one small corner of the reserve. How very important it is to identify and if necessary to map all of these more unusual and interesting species, such as the horseshoe vetch, in order to ensure that they are not overlooked in the general management of the reserve. If the 5-square-yard area of this plant were, for example, allowed to be overshadowed by a single tree or bramble bush, or if a path were diverted across it, or horse-riders allowed gradually to encroach over it as they sought less stony ascents of the hill, not only would the sole patch of horseshoe vetch be annihilated, but the sole colony of chalkhill blue butterflies as well, since the caterpillars are entirely dependent upon the foodplant. I know of hardly any other horseshoe vetch in the chalkhills nearby, although it does grow extensively on the downs in the east of Sussex.

Another peaflower, the common bird's-foot trefoil, is a habitual constituent of the chalk flora, or ought to be. Although it is easily dominated by rough tall grasses, it remains common in the reserve and grows well locally in a great variety of habitats, from slightly acid sand dunes to railway cuttings on Wealden clay. It is the foodplant of the common blue butterfly, one which nowadays is not in fact all that common. Bird's-foot trefoil is easily recognised by its bright yellow peaflowers, often prostrate, its hairless and trailing stem, and particularly by the arrangement of three pea-pods which are about an inch long and placed at angles like the toes of a bird's foot. Kidney-vetch

LONG-TAILED FIELDMOUSE

is similar, but the flowers are clustered into crowded heads and the leaves are silky and greyish. It is not nearly so common as bird's-foot trefoil but is faithful to several places scattered around the reserve from valley track-sides to steep chalky banks, and it is the foodplant of the adonis blue butterfly.

Other members of the peaflower family are the easily recognised bush vetch and tufted vetch, which straggle carelessly over brambles and rough grassland with festoons of blue or purple flowers, but they have no place in a true chalk sward. Looking rather like them, but miniaturised and of a quite different family, are the lovely little milkworts, of which two of the only five British species are found in the reserve. These flowers, appearing in May, attract perhaps more attention from the knowledgeable flower-watcher than any others except for the orchids. The curious fact is that they can be almost any colour. Common milkwort is more likely to give a range of colours, with the Oxford and Cambridge blues being the most popular. It can also produce mauve, pink, white, or white-tipped magenta. These quite small flowers are in loose clusters often prostrate and creeping low down among the grasses, the trailing stem having scattered, alternate, pointed leaves which are broadest at or below the middle. Chalk milkwort is found here too, usually a gentian blue colour, identified not so much by its flower – which can also be white, mauve or pale blue – but by the rosette of leaves. These two milkworts grow in small numbers in true chalk turf on south- and west-facing banks, but if the sheep happen to be grazing over the area you may very well not see them in their main station in the valley.

W. H. Hudson was particularly fond of eyebright, a curious little plant which, like the speedwells, is also a member of the figwort family. He made much of the fact that its roots are so minute that it can most easily be torn from the ground. The fact is, of course, that it is semi-parasitic, its host being the roots of grass. Its green or bronzy-green leaves are small, stiff and deeply toothed, the flowers, white and open, are small with falling lips, the lower with a tiny yellow spot and reddish or purple veins.

The commonest of the grasses is undoubtedly sheep's fescue, which gives the grassland its characteristic finely interwoven look, the individual blades being often no more than a millimetre wide. In heavily grazed conditions, normally coarse grass such as false oat and upright brome can also appear dwarfed and fine-leaved, and both are indeed a natural constituent of 'good' turf when kept in this state. Fine-leaved hair-grass, with its attractive glaucous leaves with a distinctive 'tramline' down the blade, is another grass which I like to see, because it is an indication that the turf is in good fettle and is not being over-grazed or trampled to death. These are the grasses of the slopes. In the valley, and on the north-facing slope beyond the tumuli, the dominant grass is downy oat-grass, with its boat-shaped blade abruptly terminated in a beautifully proportioned bow like a Northumberland coble fishing boat. Sometimes it forms dense swards with few herbs or grasses besides.

Quaking or totter grass is perhaps the best-loved grass of all and is much admired by visitors, who find it flowering in June, since it either reminds them of their childhood when it was obviously much commoner, or impresses them with their first view of it. The flower heads resemble clusters of Chinese lanterns hung from fine wire and bamboo canes. Cat's-tail and sweet vernal-grass are less easily identified until they flower, when the latter may turn some areas in the valley grasslands into a brassy sheen.

Of the herbs, salad burnet is the most easily recognisable and common of all the chalk plants in our corner of the world. If it is absent something is wrong, usually too much trampling or too long spent under tall coarse grass or bushes. It struggles on under the press of human feet for a year or two, then quickly gives out despite its long taproot. It is easily recognised by its separate leaves, finely toothed at the tips, even before it sends up a peculiar globe-like flower head on which dozens of minute red flowers shine north, south, east and west. One taste of its leaves with their cucumber-skin flavour clinches the recognition.

You will not walk far over Kingley Vale without pressing a hawkbit with your foot. These are usually rough hawkbit, which begin the season with a vaguely thistle-like rosette of leaves, rough and hairy to the touch, and end in July and August with single composite flowers sometimes so closely packed that the ground appears to have risen half a foot into a platform of golden yellow, particularly when a clearance has taken place or grazing has just ceased. Like the hawkbits, but smaller and lemon-coloured, with silvery underleaves, the attractive little mouse-ear hawkweed sometimes forms dense patches, killing off all competitors for up to 4 square yards. It seems to make the best of bad going, for it is one of those plants which are able to colonise open ground. It therefore spread well after the grazing by ponies, when bare paths were opened up in the turf following the wet winter of 1974–5. Once established, it tends to hold its ground. The yellow composites end by September with the autumn hawkbit, a mere shadow of the July glory.

Yellow is the main colour throughout high summer. After common rockrose in the highest parts of the gulley, that little cactus-like plant biting stonecrop or wall-pepper turned the whole valley yellow in 1975 after the ponies had gone. (I was even able to see a yellow glow from this hill, through binoculars, from the A27 trunk-road eight miles away.) It is of course an opportunist like mouse-ear hawkweed, but it is not quite so good at establishing itself permanently and may not be seen again in quite the same abundance. At the present time the sheep seem to be intrigued by its biting flavour after their diet of rye grass and break it about, often swallowing quite a lot of what they take.

The bane of any chalk grassland reserve is ragwort, ' a noxious weed under the meaning of the Act' which, with farmland nearby, must be removed since it can be dangerous to cattle. I started on the task in summer 1964 and have been at it ever since, aided now and then by family and friends and, of late, by the British Trust for Conservation Volunteers. What a pity that such a fine looking flower has to be destroyed. It forms a second storey of yellow above the hawkbits, a tall, branched flower 3 feet or more high, in shape rather like an ash tree. Dense golden umbels of up to a hundred flowers reflect summer-time into the face as one grasps its woody stem and pulls it with a pound or two of earth from its grip on the turf. Swarms of flies, beetles, hoverflies and bees which have been feeding on its aromatic nectar fall to the ground or settle on the clothes, wondering what has happened to their happy drunken world. Gradually, the sward becomes green again as avenues are pulled out during the hot days of July, the 'noxious' weed whose only fault is that it poisons cattle very occasionally and causes illness of the liver in horses if they eat it in great quantities – though they usually spit it out. Between fifty and seventy acres of ragwort were each year pulled out and burned on one or two pyres, an oily smoke driving off the hungry bees which return and settle almost within the flames. We have learnt to leave those plants carrying the 'caterpillars with football jerseys' – as they call the cinnabar moth larvae in country places – the black and yellow striped caterpillars which are the only larvae to prey significantly on ragwort and rely on it as their sole foodplant.

After several years of very hard work we finally called in the Conservation Corps (now the British Trust for Conservation Volunteers) who lined out in a long row and worked gravely through the, by then, somewhat depleted plants, assembling little piles of yellow flowers to be burnt at the end of the day. In only two days it was done: the reserve was green and silent again. In the summer of 1977 we put sheep into the gulley paddock. One of the first plants they went for was the ragwort, and now hardly a plant lives there.

The Conservation Corps have since made short work of the plants in

94

other areas. Some cows did die of ragwort poisoning on nearby land in 1976 (the plants were in meadowland) so the job is obviously worth while from the public relations aspect; how easily could a farmer have pointed at the reserve as the source of seed infecting his land. For the rest of the public, no more than one in a hundred knew what we were doing when they saw us tearing tall, fine, yellow-flowered plants from the ground. Now and then conscientious members remonstrated with us and tried to put a stop to it.

To many people, Richard Jefferies and W. H. Hudson among them, the harebell represents the spirit of the downs. Although larger than many of the tiny flowers which compose chalk grassland, it has more grace and style. It is the hue of summer skies over the hill, its bell shakes and nods in July currents which buoy the swifts high above. Its leaves are finely fern-like, the stem no more than a thread. North Country people call it the bluebell, for it grows on limestone moors and dry heaths up there, but it is nothing like the fleshy southern bluebell of damp woods. Its tall, rough cousin is nettle-leaved bellflower, with dark blue bells as big as the little brass sheep-bells I saw in the Afghanistan highlands. The odd plant grows here and there faithfully year after year, with its triangular pointed leaves, rough like a nettle. But the one which the botanists come for is clustered bellflower. A mere dozen plants cluster on the ground along the western flank, flowering after mid-summer with a striking, handsome violet flower like a gentian, these too clustering on the stems, so that the total effect is like a small posy of violets lying on the bank. At the present, these few precious plants are threatened by the tread of horses' hooves when riders spread to the side of the track to avoid the flints, and it is hoped that temporary notices and hawthorn slips strategically placed will keep them to the straight and narrow.

Venus's looking-glass is another bellflower which is fairly rare and comes within a few yards of being on the reserve by appearing just over the boundary, so I include it here. It usually grows in the edge of the corn field a few feet from the south-eastern boundary, one year accompanying no less than three separate species of poppies there. It is a curious, hairy little plant with unstalked, oblong, wavy leaves, and grows no more than a few inches high. In cloudy weather its petal-like corolla tubes close up, showing pale undersides.

Pride of place, however, of all the bellflowers, goes to the only two plants of round-headed rampion, which had been thought to be extinct on Kingley Vale. In the extreme south-east corner of the reserve there was an area of extremely poor grassland overshadowed largely by thick bushes. Donkeys were about to be enclosed within this area to browse and graze, in an experiment to try and reclaim the relict turf. As far as I knew donkeys had never before been tried out for reclaiming chalk grassland, but it was known that they were voracious eaters, and I had watched them in the Middle East attack any standing plant they could reach. They are less selective than ponies and also have the advantage of being lighter and smaller-hooved. It was a hot July day when, having been playing with barbed wire for several days and having finally finished enclosing the three-acre paddock, I began the next job of recording the plants between fixed points, so that we would have a scientific record of what happened under the muzzles of the real donkey-workers.

The grassland which I was recording was dull to say the least: practically a pure sward of 3-foot-high cocksfoot or false oat, with a few common wasteland herbs such as yarrow, well scattered and forming no more than 5 per cent of the total cover. Then, suddenly, as I parted the grass to look down into one square yard frame, there was this lovely blue flower, reminiscent of a cornflower. I had found *Phyteuma* on the reserve at last, having searched for her these many years. It was an exciting moment. The next year she didn't appear, but that was the severe drought of 1976 when few plants were recognisable in the recording season. In 1977 she was there again; the flower had been bitten off by one of the donkeys but the leaves were healthy. Also in 1977 another site was found for *Phyteuma* on one of the mown meadows on the plateau.

The teasel family, too, though best known for its leader whose skeletons are collected for ornament, has small and delicate plants that evoke summer days rather than winter hedgerows. Thus small scabious signals the high heat of summer, sweaty days of August when sea fogs roll in from Chichester harbour and the grassland has a tired grey-green or brown colour and the last of the flowers are opening. There is one dense patch of this pale blue composite flower with fern-like finely cut leaves (half of this 3-square-yard colony was destroyed by a man with a metal detector and a trowel, who was searching for the fag ends of war in summer 1975), and single plants or much smaller colonies are found here and there. Butterflies flock to the small scabious, and the blues are lost in their own colour.

Much taller and bolder is the field scabious which grows with the dead-nettles along banks on the way into the reserve. But the pride of the family is devil's-bit scabious whose roots, as every countryman knows, were bitten off by the devil, being very short (though if anybody digs one up to see, the same thing may happen to him!). The elliptical leaves are

Part of the 'sinister and fantastic' forest beloved of the Victorians. Even on the hottest day the temperature will be 10° cooler under the dense canopy formed by these very old yews.

Above: The gnarled trunk of one of the great yews, probably five hundred years old.
Below: Stages in downland succession. Juniper bushes have colonised turf, while beyond them yews have grown above their juniper 'nurses'.

Above: Part of the younger yew forest colonising chalk grassland. (Note the ant-hills in the foreground.)
Below: Scrub clearing by British Trust for Conservation Volunteers.

A picnic party in Kingley Vale in the 1880s.

Above: Two of the reserve's rarer orchids. The autumn lady's tresses (left) grows in open downland and the fly orchid (right) on the edges of woodland.
Below: The round-headed rampion (left) is almost extinct in Kingley Vale, but the common ragwort (right) grows in such profusion that it has to be destroyed.

One of the specialities of the reserve is the curious bee orchid, whose flower so closely resembles a bee (see pp. 118–19).

Above: *The privet hawk moth, seen here having just emerged from its pupa.*
Below: *The brimstone butterfly is one of the first to emerge, and has been seen on the reserve as early as the first week in February.*

Kestrels are seen hunting for grasshoppers in late summer, hovering on the 'wind funnel' currents above the main gully.

Above: The badger, due to local persecution, has temporarily vanished from its centuries-old setts on the reserve.

Below: Common shrews are some of the few mammals which feed on yew berries. Water shrews have also been recorded in Kingley Vale.

The hare lives on the reserve during winter and moves to neighbouring fields in the summer.

Pioneering experiments were carried out to reclaim grassland from scrub and rough grass. New Forest ponies were tried first, seen (above) eating dogwood scrub. Donkeys (below) were even more successful, as their small hooves were less destructive to the turf.

Foxes have greatly increased on Kingley Vale in recent years, but their effect on populations of ground-nesting birds has not yet been determined.

A fallow buck ruminating in high summer (note the flies clustered around its antlers, always bothersome at this time).

Above: An aerial view of the main valley, once known as Kingly Bottum.
Below: The field museum. Part of the display is the work of school children who have visited the reserve; underneath is a cross-section of a yew trunk.

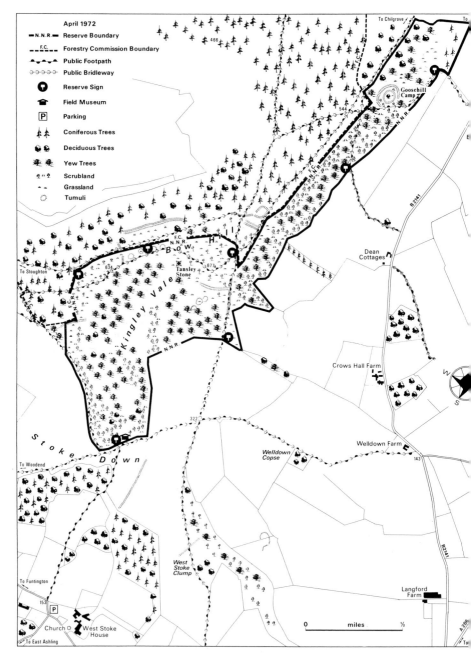

April 1972

N.N.R. Reserve Boundary

F.C. Forestry Commission Boundary

Public Footpath

Public Bridleway

Reserve Sign

Field Museum

P Parking

Coniferous Trees

Deciduous Trees

Yew Trees

Scrubland

Grassland

Tumuli

To Chilgrove

Goosehill Camp

B 2141

Dean Cottages

Crows Hall Farm

N N R

N.N.R.

F.C. N.N.R. BOW

Tansley Stone

Kingley Vale

To Stoughton

H I L L

544

466

634

674

322

Stoke Down

To Woodend

Welldown Copse

Welldown Farm

143

West Stoke Clump

Langford Farm

To Funtington

153

P

Church

West Stoke House

To East Ashling

0   miles   ½

B 2141

A 286

A map of Kingley Vale and the surrounding countryside.

rough and hairy, and not unlike those of the wild teasel. But the flowers are like deep blue cushions on the ends of their slender stem, with 70 or 80 flowers crammed together. The plant is not very common on the reserve, occurring in a fringe around the edges of the plateau where the clay cap provides acid soil, and is best seen below the Tansley Stone. It is valuable as being the foodplant of the marsh fritillary butterfly, which used to live on Kingley Vale some years ago but had not been recorded for some time. However, recently some stock was reared nearby, and having obtained the necessary permit we released 20–30 butterflies in Kingley Vale, as well as some caterpillars which were fed on to the devil's bit scabious. We await the result.

There are tiny colonies of many flowers on the reserve which have no real place in the rather élite community of the chalk turf but which cling in the no-man's-land of 'wasteland and dry places'. Not particularly rare, but attractive and eye-catching, they add much to the casual visitor's ramble on a summer weekend, and since they do not impinge on the purity of the sward in any way, I protect them as far as I can by keeping vehicle wheels off them, perhaps cutting back a little rough grass or an overhanging shrub; 'gardening', I admit, and not strictly useful in the true dynamics of the reserve – but we all have our idiosyncracies. One such plant is restharrow, another vervain, a third is goatsbeard. All are greeted like old friends as the seasons come and go.

Orchids

Orchids are a most fascinating study. Each one has its own story to tell. They are the aristocrats of the flower world: particular in habitat, temperamental in appearance, and with exacting sexual requirements.

In the early days I spent a lot of time protecting orchids from the then common habit of the public of picking the flower spikes, and virtually stopped it altogether by 1967. But rabbits and sheep love orchid flowers and must have grazed them for centuries, yet they survived, and many old, established lawns suddenly sprouted orchids in the war when they were no longer cut. Little is known yet about the factors involved in their life-cycle.

All orchids are 'fickle' plants with variable flowering or appearance, and this must be largely due to the delicate balance by which they exist. First, their seeds are so small – more the appearance of fine dust than anything – that they are unable to produce a green shoot for a number of years, depending on the species. This may be about three years for the early purple, six for the bee, and up to twenty-two for the lady's slipper. For this interval of years the fertile seed is growing in the soil into a reasonable size that can send a thin green shoot skywards. To grow it has to eat, and it feeds on a particular fungus with which it has a symbiotic relationship, the orchid seed allowing the fungus to digest part of itself in the process. Thus before any orchid seed can propagate it must fall on the type of ground in which the fungus is able to live. Apparently this situation is not common, the great majority of the seeds falling on 'barren' ground. When the orchid does find suitable land, new plants will mark the spot year after year by successful establishment.

Why then, do apparently suitable places fail to produce a continual population? Back in the 1960s we all thought that the orchid only needed freedom from trampling and picking. Now there seems to be more to the problem. Having looked very carefully at all the areas where die-back seems to be most marked, it seems that what they all have in common is an enrichment of soil, either by tall grasses falling back on to the soil instead of being carried away by mowing or grazing, or by too great an amount of droppings from grazing animals. A certain early purple colony suffered from both complaints, the overgrowth of tall grass dating from 1967, the droppings of our ponies from 1971. Both dates coincide with a marked decline of plants. The ponies chose the general area of the plot as one of their 'latrines', though no more than about three piles of droppings were to be seen over the 100-square-yard plot at any one time. This presumably was enough to cause the demise of the fungal agent, which appears to require a relatively impoverished soil, judging by the presence of orchids on dry, thin, well-drained soils. (This is why orchids when uprooted and planted in gardens hardly ever last for long.) Now all important orchid sites on the reserve are mown every year, and the dead grass is removed.

One factor over which one has no control is climate, and orchid numbers respond to the changes that occur from year to year. A glance at the tables of numbers in the Appendix on pages 177–8 shows how closely all the plants responded to a warm wet winter in 1974–5 followed by a warm dry spell in 1975. A dry winter followed by a dry spring in 1976 did not generally improve the numbers, and the severe heat shrivelled up many plants before they had the chance to set seeds. But the full orchid story is told species by species.

Early Purple

Of the eleven species of orchid present on the reserve, the commonest and the first to flower is the early purple. The leaf rosettes may appear in the turf in the first half of March, and I remember the excitement with which I discovered the first purple-spotted, waxy, shiny leaves in the valley, on 12 March 1964, during my honeymoon. (There could not have been a better way to spend a honeymoon than gently botanising, and I recommend it to anyone.) My wife was particularly fascinated to watch the bees which visited these flowers coming away with little knobs on their heads, like miniature clubs. These are the pollinia, which are the pollen-bearing sacs. They attach themselves to the bee's head when the bee alights to drink the nectar, by pushing against it and exposing sticky viscidia (cemented discs). This hardens very quickly, like Araldite glue. The bee moves on, and the pollinia change from an upright position to a horizontal one – thus when the bee enters another flower the pollen-bearing sac is held 'at the ready', and pollination can take place. This anecdote has a sting in the tail, however. Over the years we have found many a distressed bee, feebly waving its legs towards a dozen or so pollinia attached around the eyes and thereby blinding the unsuspecting transport carrier.

The early purple orchid is so numerous that I do not attempt to count individuals, but estimate that between two and three thousand flowers are showing most years by 1 May. They are faithful to the same banks and meadow edges year after year, but there seems no doubt that they have been generally declining over the past thirteen years. Accidents constantly befall them, such as the late frost in April 1967 which killed the flower heads of all the valley orchids, and the cold winds of 1977 which caused many flowers to shrivel before being able to set seed. Snails, rabbits and pheasants, as well as humans, destroy flowers and leaves each year.

I mapped one colony over a period of ten years. It showed a steady decline in numbers from 49 plants flowering or otherwise in 1964, to nil in 1972. All but 3 of the 49 plants which I first saw in 1964 died out and were never seen again. By the following year 38 entirely new plants were standing within a few inches of their predecessors, but I would never have believed that the colony could have shifted itself about so completely had I not accurately placed each one. These 38 survived for four years in comparative tranquility: a settled era in the life of orchids.

Common Twayblade

The next orchid to bloom is the twayblade – the two-leaved. Only two plants have been found on the reserve, though it is quite common nearby in old coppice and beech woodland (half a dozen plants flower each May on my lawn). When the flowers on their foot-high stem are produced, a close look will reveal a dozen or more little green men hanging there. The likeness is remarkable – head, arms, chest, legs in perfect proportion. It is much like the man orchid that does grow in Sussex but not on Kingley Vale. The whole plant including the flowers is pale green.

Both plants were on east-facing banks of short chalk turf, one on the east and the other on the west side of the reserve. One plant flowered continuously from 1964 to 1970 before dying out. The other flowered once in 1971 and then managed only a pair of leaves for the next six years. The twayblade, unlike other orchids, certainly seems to require a shaded, rather damp soil, and one where a 're-processing' of the soil occurs, as for instance the site on a steep bank under old sycamore trees near the reserve where rabbits throw out a continual stream of loose chalk rubble. Their scarcity on the reserve is probably due to the lack of high, deciduous canopy coupled with moist calcareous soil. Yew canopy is obviously too shady for any orchid species to grow, and the ground underneath too dry.

Spotted Orchid

Mid-June sees the first flower spike of the spotted orchid rise from the glaucous-coloured leaves with their leopard spots. Clusters of pale lilac flowers with purple speckles stand on the banks – sometimes in the same areas as the early purple, but more often in select, tightly packed little colonies which have no other orchid anywhere near them. Such a colony is found on the east-facing slope of the extension to the reserve, in Cp. 18. It occupies a mere 20 × 10 yard area of good short turf around a small yew tree. A few invading brambles can be kept cut back, and a tuft or two of false oat grass is annually pulled out of the plot to stop it seeding and spreading.

Other colonies of spotted orchid are widely scattered throughout the reserve and there is much annual fluctuation in their numbers. Factors involved in this could be climate, or widespread grazing régimes (as last seen under rabbits, which affected the whole reserve), or other uncontrollable events, but no one as yet knows the real answer. The colonies of this orchid all have one thing in common – they are on east-facing slopes, where the turf is short and generally controlled by the shallow soils.

Fragrant Orchid

At about the same time as the spotted orchid or a few days later, this graceful pink orchid with its sweet hyacinth or carnation smell blooms in only one compartment. It can be distinguished not only by its scent but by the long, thin, semi-circular spur or nectar-carrier. These are even more loyal to their positions than other orchids, the main colony occurring in just ten square yards of turf in the bottom of an old sunken track or drift which, having been blocked off by yew further along has not been used by horses or humans for fifty years. In its best year, 1975, which was also good for the bee orchid, it appeared in the same areas but in greater numbers.

The colonies are all in gullies or sunken tracks of varying sizes – one is an old wartime tank track a foot deep and wide. This seems to suggest that the plant needs a supply of relatively fresh chalk in which certain minerals still occur that have not yet been leached away by rain. It needs years for the seed development. It is visited largely at night by moths, the pollinia being stuck on to their proboscises and carried safely into each flower as a result. One look at the extremely slender spur, curled like an eyelash, will show how well adapted is the long tongue of the moth to get inside it. I have not seen spurs cut open by bees, wasps or beetles as in other flowers, but it is certain that they could not get to the nectar otherwise.

Fly Orchid

This mysterious little plant is confined to one small part of the reserve where it grows in short turf on an east-facing slope surrounded by yew trees. A couple of dozen flowers are all that are seen and they bloom early in June and quickly fade away. All *Ophrys* orchids have a large furry or velvety lower petal called the lips or labellum. These lips strikingly remind one of an insect, and in the case of the fly orchid it is a slim, beautiful insect, coloured purplish brown with a band of shining, pale blue across its body and two projections like antennae at the top of the lip where it joins the stem. The flower actually resembles a rare wasp (*Gorytes mystaceus*), and it blooms early when only the male wasp has emerged. He courts the flower and lands upon it in an attempt to mate, exchanging pollinia between flowers and thus fertilising the orchid. (The phrase 'pseudo-copulation' has been dreamed up by scientists to describe this rather pathetic Copelia farce, looking at it from the wasp's viewpoint.) But the ingenuity of natural development which has brought the flower to this stage of mimicry, where it can trade on one wasp's fleeting moments of desire, makes one feel not only deeply impressed but savagely protective towards such examples of the complexity of evolution.

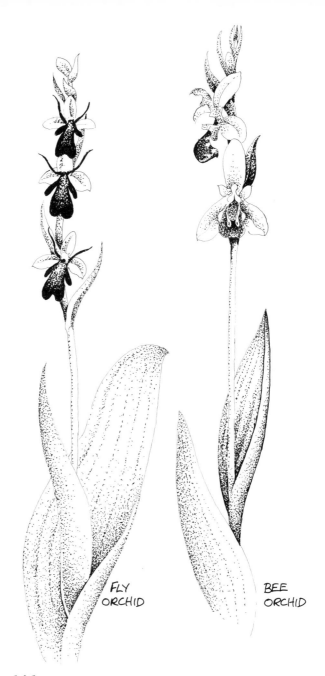

FLY
ORCHID

BEE
ORCHID

Bee Orchid

The bee orchid, another *Ophrys* species, is undoubtedly our most treasured and spectacular orchid, and many people come each June and July to see and photograph the strange flower which looks so like a furry brown bee.

Most of the plants grow within a few feet of well-used tracks and paths: the best colony occurs densely on one particular patch of recently disturbed (c. 1940s) soil in Cp. 13 where, one imagines, a tank slewed itself around, grinding away the top six inches of soil. Here, within 16 square yards, 30–35 plants are always found, and they have never failed even when other colonies (particularly in Cp. 9b) in short unbroken turf have come and gone.

Bee orchids in other areas might be encouraged too, by some judicious management or 'gardening'. I am thinking particularly of the plants in Cp. 5 which grow scattered all the way down the track (now used by the nature trail) around the western edge of the reserve. Many of the plants grow on the south side, within a few feet or even inches of small projecting bushes or the stumps of bushes. In other words, as you walk down the trail there are hidden behind many a little yew bush, birch sapling or clump of low scrub, bee orchids which it is very easy to miss altogether. If you walk the wrong way around the trail you will be more likely to see the flowers (which are at their best in the last week of June). Does this mean that the plants are protected from passing feet, or that they get just that little extra reflected sun? Judging by those that grow on the tumuli, the latter is the essential fact. Other thoughts that come to mind are that the soil fungus related to the roots of the shrubs at these points helps the orchid plants. If it is all merely a question of shelter and heat (other conditions being favourable) then all one has to do is to encourage sheltering shrubs at intervals on the sides of the track. These would be useful too in funnelling people and particularly horses' sliding hooves in wet weather and keeping them off the banks. But the effects of such an experiment would probably not be seen for many years.

Pyramid Orchid

This is the orchid of high summer on the downs, coming at the same time as the red clover and therefore often being reported at 'new sites' far and wide around the reserve, sometimes even by those who should know better! In fact like all orchids, it is extremely local in its choice of site and can be found in the same old places year after year. In general, it occupies the kind of bank favoured by frog and bee orchids, but it is more widely distributed thereon, and in one case, in Cp. 9, it is the only orchid growing at that place.

The clustered deep pink flowers form a pyramid at the very top of their stem which may be 6–12 inches high. Anyone stupid enough to pick the flowers will regret it for they will find that they have a smell like a fox or a tom-cat in their house (this is the same with other orchids, particularly the early purple). The sepals are hooded and curve around the three-lobed lip, and the spur is a long, thin, curved tube like that of the fragrant orchid, suitable only for the long tongues of moths and butterflies. But, beware butterfly! The sticky pad, or viscidium, will coil tightly around the tongue and become extremely uncomfortable. I have seen a small heath butterfly with three sets of pollinia attached, sitting with obvious discomfort on a grass stem, unable to retract its tongue and rolling and unrolling the proboscis.

Conservation of the pyramid orchid is straightforward – it requires long grass to be cut or grazed away from its chosen niche. Those in Cp. 9 were apparently dying out from overshadowing by upright brome grass, until in 1971 the ponies began to graze there and the orchids quickly returned. Sheep grazing in 1977 (April–June) and some rabbit grazing meant that the flowers were eaten off before they were counted, but a good number were noticed in bud and some 50 leaf rosettes are there. Cp. 5c is largely mown by lawn-mower when required. Cp. 5a is not touched, being in the same sunken trackway as a number of fragrant orchids where they are not particularly overgrown by coarse grass, but having just enough cover to have limited the over-powering effects of the drought of 1976. This lovely cool flower flourished in 1975: the banks of Cp. 5c looked almost like a poppy field in the first week of July.

Greater Butterfly Orchid

This beautiful creamy-coloured flower is more common elsewhere in the edges of woodland along the South Downs than on Kingley Vale, where only two or three plants flower year after year under the edge of a yew tree. Periodically, encroaching scrub of bramble and dogwood is cut back all around the flowers. The two leaves are large and tapering and firmly press themselves domineeringly over other competing vegetation, even though they are soft and much frailer than most rosette plants. The flowers are heavily fragrant especially at night when, as with the fragrant orchid, moths visit them and the pollinia become attached to their heads.

Large White Helleborine

Until 1977 there was no record of this plant on the reserve, but in early June I almost stepped on the two white tapering flowers of this 'egg orchid' or 'poached egg plant' as it is called locally (there are orange coloured blotches on the lip resembling the yolks of eggs). It was growing in a drift of beech leaves in a very dark place, shaded to the south by a yew, and the nearest green plant was five yards away. It was

AUTUMN LADY'S TRESSES

therefore very stunted and weak and not at all like the upright flower spikes with their five or six flowers the size of kingfishers' eggs which normally grow in open shade in this wood. This was the eleventh species of orchid to be found on the reserve in my fourteen years and it was an exciting moment.

Frog Orchid

This is by far the commonest orchid, blooming, if that is the word, in thousands in all the short turf of tracksides girdling and circling the east and west sides of the reserve. Yet few people ever see the little greenybronze spike with its six to eight flowers which look so like a stunted grass stem. An exceptional plant may be 8 inches tall. More usually the spike is 2–3 inches and nestles hidden in that slightly tawny green turf of July and August. Individual flowers have hooded sepals and the lip is tongue-shaped and forked at the tip. It grows well on the tumuli with the five bee orchids, but it succumbs quickly to overshadowing by tall grasses and so flourishes on the lawn-mowered banks.

Autumn Lady's Tresses

This orchid species is locally common on lawns and grassy places along the coastal plain, so the fact that only one plant appears in Kingley Vale (in Cp. 8) and that only sporadically, suggests that it needs the influence of sea breezes. It is a most delightful plant with small scented white flowers in a single twisted row and very easily overlooked, like a shy girl with white bows interwoven into her long plait.

Management

None of this chalk grassland area would exist without very careful active management.

In the past grazing by sheep and rabbits kept large areas open to grassland, inhibiting the growth of scrub and the development of yew forest. Sheep were not fenced in as they are today. In the 1920s and 1930s they were free to roam about everywhere under the yew trees, as shepherds of that time have told me, the sheep never taking any harm from yew browsing. The turf of fifty years ago was somewhat different in character: it was covered with far more chalk scree (appearing 50 per cent white in aerial photographs of 1933), and there were almost no ant hillocks.

The remarkable individuality of ant-hills, each with their own particular composition of different flowers, was first seen after the war and particularly in the years immediately following myxomatosis, when many plants were for once allowed to blossom unchecked by grazing. It was not long, however, before they began to vanish as tall grasses also unchecked by grazing began to flower for the first time in recent history. Their seed spread quickly through the small glades and they had no competitors until the scrub began to take hold. It was at this period of great transition that the means at last became available for active management – not by grazing this time but by mechanical cutting.

Experience of removing rough tall grass mechanically was gained at

Lullington Heath, near Seaford, another reserve for which I am responsible. Methods tried out there were not necessarily of use at Kingley Vale but the knowledge gained allowed those of us concerned in planning the management programme to make decisions on how to implement it in the best way.

In 1968, five years since I had become warden, a beaten-up faded red Massey-Ferguson tractor was bought for us by the N.C.C. in Kent for £25. She was christened Betsy. A low-loader trailer, easily drawn by a Landrover, was also purchased, as well as a brand-new silage cutter for the (then) tremendous price of £175.

The Chief Warden Brian Phillips arrived with Betsy on the trailer one October afternoon, and to my eyes her faded paintwork gleamed in the fine autumn afternoon sunshine. The seat was a bit tattered after a dozen seasons out in the Kent weather, her tyres were lacerated by spinning into the Wealden mud and her exhaust stack was bent. But these were honourable battle scars.

After a short tow by the Landrover, Betsy chuffed vapourised diesel like a Welsh quarry steam-engine out of her funnel, barked and blew the insides of her silencer up into a brown mushroom cloud, which descended as a fine dust on to the face and hands of myself, the driver. She had six forward gears and she pulled willingly in all of them. A day later Brian returned with the silage-cutter and we connected them together. Betsy whirled the 28 metal hammers on their axle at 13,000 revs with no fuss when she was warmed up. The silage cutter trembled and we stood back from it in awe. At last some real management was about to begin! I had borrowed a trailer into which to collect the grass, and with this sweeping the leaves from overhanging boughs, I trundled up into the valley.

I wanted to cut about two acres of valley grassland first of all. It was an area which had once been dominated by fescue grass that had formed small tufts when grazed by rabbits. But now this meadow was dominated by downy oat grass, upright brome and to a lesser extent false oat grass. I engaged the cutter and started into the rough. In places it was three feet high with several scattered bushes of blackthorn, hawthorn and dogwood. The tractor climbed over tufts of grass which formed hummocks of roots a foot high. Then it would plunge down into old hidden rabbit warrens which were like mortar bomb craters. A steady stream of black smoke and sparks roared out of the chimney. I cut a wide square through the most accessible part of this valley and then started on the second lap. We were going fine, although in the bottom of our six gears it was very slow, but then my inexperience caught up with me. I had nearly three-quarters of a load behind of damp grass and mud from churned-up ant-heaps, and instead of emptying this before going on again into the worst part which was slightly uphill I pressed on. Suddenly Betsy was spinning, her left wheel up against an ant-heap, her right in a rabbit hole. Nothing would make her move.

The next morning I disconnected the cutter and tried to tow the trailer away. But it had settled into the ground. There was nothing for it but to tip its load out into the meadow, as the farmer wanted his trailer back the next day. The ton or more of heating grass had now to be removed bit by bit in the back of the Landrover. The problem was where to put it. We could not dump it just anywhere for it would cause a severe nutrient build-up which would encourage patches of nettles and thistles to flourish. As silage it was useless, having too many flints and earth lumps. Finally, I chose a dump on a hidden patch of ground behind a yew tree.

So the cutting continued throughout the winter, though all of the five-acre area on the hills had to be raked by hand because Betsy would not pull the heavy silage trailer up to the plateau. The raking took the best part of a fortnight. Eventually a small grass trailer based on a Morris Traveller axle was made by a local blacksmith for £50 and with this I removed many tons of grass. The slow part of the cutting job was to unload this trailer since it was not designed to tip up. The grass layered itself and was almost impossible to pick out except in the exact reverse order. This was solved by placing a metal grid at the front of the trailer, with a wire hawser coiled up on the floor attached to it. When the time came to unload, the end of the steel rope was attached to the draw-bar of the Landrover which was then driven off as fast as possible. When it had gone twenty yards it came to the end of the rope and the grid was pulled out with a jerk, catapulting the ton of grass well away from the trailer.

Betsy was a remarkable machine, often running for hours on virtually no water and very little oil when these ran out faster than I expected. I once had to top her up with tea when she suddenly boiled and blew a jet of steam ten feet into the air. Several times she nearly turned over. After three years of severe work it was thought a good idea to have the engine rebored, with new mains and pistons. The estimate was £500 at 1971 prices so the idea was shelved; Betsy went back to work and continued for another three years, when she was officially pensioned off and a new tractor arrived. Betsy had halted the spread of brome grass on Kingley Vale and the new tractor has merely to skim off an ever-decreasing crop. The loads of 'silage' never became the embarrassment that we feared. They have always been dumped in the same places year after year and

124

have virtually disappeared, one growing a small crop of nettles which harbours small tortoiseshell butterflies, another growing the reserve's only colony of blewit toadstools, the third feeding several fallow deer throughout the cold frosty winter of December 1976.

The point of this mechanical cutting was to kiil off the rank grasses such as upright brome grass and to encourage the spread of the chalk sward. Its effect on particular areas is analysed in the Appendix.

The Birds

Winter Bird Populations

The winter bird populations are dominated by two family groups, the thrushes and the titmice. The berry crop of yew and hawthorn (and to a lesser extent of spindle, privet and dogwood), which lasts from August to mid-December, draws in as many as 2000 redwings and fieldfares from about mid-October onwards. These then disperse during January to April on to neighbouring meadowlands, or sometimes into deciduous woodland, to search for slugs. But the first arrivals in search of arils are locally bred mistle thrushes, which flock in from mid-July onwards in maximum numbers of 250 and may stay until Christmas or even later, helping the foreign birds to clear up remaining holly and hawthorn berries. Continental song thrushes and blackbirds may also appear during autumn, as well as local birds. In fact, in some years song thrushes have been more numerous than the others.

The thrushes are concentrated in the valley and on the eastern side of Bow Hill, where they are sheltered from the roughest prevailing weather. At dusk many of them go to roost over the hill on the north side, or into old hawthorns and yew on the plateau, and it is then easy enough to count them against the western sky. The temperature on the lee side of these hills is always a degree or two warmer than elsewhere, and the wind will often influence the choice of site. There are usually two pairs of sparrowhawks overwintering in the immediate area and they prey continually on thrushes; the remains of one plucked body is found each day on average, giving at least 100 thrushes taken in the 150-acre valley alone each winter. Tawny owls also take some birds, as shown in their pellets, although their main diet is mice and earthworms.

Resident mistle thrushes, some using spring and early summer breeding territories, maintain winter territories throughout, guarding for themselves favourite yew bushes or lone holly trees, fighting off the foreign birds if they attempt to land and eat the berries. They will not eat these berries until later winter when there is little food, and the farming or guarding work then really pays off. By late January cock

REDWING

mistle thrushes are, in any case, forming spring territories, and the berry trees are always in their areas. Song thrushes too begin territory marking in December and even November, when the two or three resident birds soon distinguish themselves from the twenty or thirty migrant birds.

Along a set route on the winter transects, surveyed twice per month from October to February inclusive, the most common bird (that is the species which registers the most frequent number of sightings or 'hearings' within a 50-yard-wide belt) is usually the fieldfare for the first three months, closely followed by the blackbird; after the New Year the blackbird becomes more common than any other bird. In some years, redwings have taken the lead from fieldfares; in 1966 they formed 67 per cent of the total bird community at their peak count in mid-November. In other years they drop to equal the numbers of blackbirds, mistle thrushes, robins and great tits. The majority of thrushes are found in the valley, despite the weather. As the transect follows the valley woodland edge it is probable that optimum thrush counts are made since there are more berries on trees standing more in the open. The drawbacks of the transect method of quantitative recording is that smaller birds, particularly the wren, goldcrest and dunnock, are not easily disturbed or seen at all if they are happily pecking about in the undergrowth or foliage, so their recorded numbers may be accidentally lower than the more noticeable thrushes.

The titmice family have at times swamped the records. In February 1973 the count revealed 91 per cent of titmice which consisted of 44 long-tailed tits, 23 great tits, 18 blue tits, 17 coal tits and 11 marsh tits. Greater numbers of all the latter four species of titmice have been recorded on one single transect when their numbers were down to 68 per cent of the overall bird population. Titmice are usually encountered in one or two large roving parties. As the transect has to be walked at a set pace it is not possible to stop, for instance, to watch a party cross the track in front, so one walks 'through' a large party of perhaps 100 birds strung out over an area wider than 50 yards. The fact that most of the valley titmice may be concentrated into this one flock therefore gives a low reading – particularly if it so happens that the party is not encountered at all on the route. However, more often than not they are, as the transect route was planned to cover the kinds of areas where they usually congregate.

Titmice feed on yew nuts in winter, splitting open the shells by hammering them after they have been wedged into crevices of the yew bark. Acorns and hawthorn shells are likewise split open and ash keys too are eaten. No systematic recording of feeding has been attempted, but wood-boring insects and bark-crawling fauna seem to be the main target for feeding when nut crops have been exhausted. Since the reserve has plenty of dead timber, particularly ash wood, this provides a rich supply of food, although the exceptional acorn yields of 1976 kept all the titmice happy through the whole winter, as did mast in the beechwoods. Long-tailed tits are largely bark and canopy feeders, finding overwintering larvae and spiders in oak and ash trees. Yew foliage has not much to offer insectivorous birds, although the peeling bark with its many crevices has a moderate spider population.

Now and then large flocks of finches dominate a transect. They are

FIELDFARES

always present somewhere in the vicinity, either within the woodland or in fields neighbouring the reserve, though the huge wintering flocks of linnets, chaffinches and greenfinches of the mid-1960s are no longer seen. The largest field flock was estimated at close on 2000 birds in January 1966. By January 1976 the same field held 185 birds of mixed species for three weeks, which was described by one young ornithologist as 'staggering'!

This downward trend may well be due to a different farming practice on this particular land, which also has resulted in the loss of our one and only wintering hen harrier that was always present up until 1975. Prior to this date root crops were often grown as cover for pheasants. The kale being planted in early spring, the ground was left fairly open for much of the early summer, until the plants grew up in early autumn into a closed canopy. Weeds, particularly fat hen, were able to profit by this open ground and they could come to maturity quicker than the kale, so that by October masses of fat hen seed was available over scores of acres. At the height of the pheasant-rearing bonanza in the early 1970s fields of mustard were planted with the same object and the same result, these being left until after Christmas before they were ploughed in. The finches swooped on the fields and were secure all winter, and one, sometimes two, harriers were in attendance.

But the farmer became too old to shoot and lost interest in the sport, and so he concentrated on the early cereal crops which resulted in wide open deserts all winter. The finches and the harriers have left. These finches would often come into the reserve: the south-east corner particularly was a favourite place for chaffinches. Every year 150 of them would be found there, some breaking into song in February when there would be great skirmishes with the resident cocks. To compensate for this decline, however, there was in 1976–7 the largest flock of greenfinches ever seen during the winter, 200-plus living in the valley and feeding on yew and hawthorn pips from the enormous harvest following the drought. Normally their numbers range between about 2 and 10 per cent of the totals and they do not appear until mid-winter. Now and then hawfinches are seen, but they are such quiet and secretive birds that quite probably they are often missed.

In recent years robins have increased and, since both male and female may sing as they form territories, there is quite a chorus by October when the winter territories are claimed. Interestingly, a count of singing robins in October does not produce double the number of birds heard in spring, when only males are singing, as one might have expected. There are indeed more robins, but only marginally so and this is probably due

130

to dispersal as well as late summer mortality.

Dunnocks, wrens and goldcrests figure well down the list of 'contacts' on these transects, but this is probably because of their secretive nature. If one could spend a lot of time in one spot (which a warden does not have time to do), no doubt they would be found to be more numerous than the transect shows. There is, for instance, a goldcrest in the yew tree in my garden throughout the winter: occasionally he gives a burst of song which I may hear once a week, but otherwise there is nothing to show he is there. Most of these birds must surely be residents, for their numbers are well documented in the summer breeding census.

Woodpeckers are present throughout the winter, particularly the green woodpecker which feeds largely on the common yellow hill ant dug out of the ant-hills which cover the chalk grassland. There are also great numbers of beetle larvae for them in the dead ash wood. Nuthatches are absent, strangely enough, and very few tree creepers are seen. Woodpigeon numbers may equal those of the fieldfare on occasion, though of course they do not come into the wood in their greatest flocks until dusk, when from late November to just into the New Year there may be as many as a thousand at a time. Sometimes they will flight back into the reserve at midday for an hour on calm, dry days when they have been able to feed well all morning (usually on winter-sown grain, clover leys, kale or hedgerow fruits, including acorns in nearby oakwoods). Pigeons, like ragwort, have to be controlled if we are to be taken as serious land users, so they are shot periodically on flight lines as they pass across our boundary. By February, as local crops dwindle, they have moved on, only a score or so of birds remaining.

The carrion crow, although not normally gregarious, also uses the reserve as a dormitory. Its numbers have steadily dwindled from a peak of 176 birds present all winter in 1967 to four birds in 1977. This dramatic decline reflects the renewed interest in gamekeeping in the area, even though pheasant shooting has somewhat decreased. Other Corvidae include the magpie, with usually at least half a dozen birds overwintering in the 100-year-old yew forest at Kingley Vale (Cp. 10). Jays confine themselves to the oak trees in the valley, but there are no more than half a dozen throughout the whole winter. They are largely responsible for the spreading of acorns and I have watched their habit of taking them out from the woods and burying them an inch deep in the chalk turf. An example of the jay's seed-spreading activity can be seen at the end of the nature trail on the western slope, and individual oaks are continually sprouting all over the chalk grassland (usually deer or hares nip them off in their first year). Rooks and jackdaws avoid the reserve in winter and only once, in 1969, did starlings attempt a large-scale winter roost. Luckily the local gamekeeper was there at the time, having spent a week repelling the 10,000 birds from his own woods nearby at West Stoke. The enormous flock settled in the yews at the southern end of the reserve, weighing down the branches. Running to the scene the gamekeeper fired shot after shot into them, and just before dusk they rose and flew right away. Had they settled there overnight they would have been more difficult to remove, and long-term effects on the yews may have been damaging.

There is generally a small flock of meadow pipits wintering in the rough grass around the tumuli, although recently these have declined to four birds or less, probably because of the grass-cutting time being altered from June to November over the whole of this hilltop. Skylarks are hardly ever seen in winter nowadays for the same reason, and a nagging worry in my mind is that the churning hammers of the Silamaster as opposed to the reciprocating cutters of old times are damaging to insect life in meadows, which means that there is little or no insect life for these two meadow-feeding birds either. On the other hand there is at least one bird which can exploit the specialised fauna of the dry grass-heaps left over from cutting and which moulder away year after year – the pied wagtail. From December 1976 about thirty fed regularly on the heap in the western meadow, catching flies and picking larvae disturbed by fallow deer that had fed there overnight. Hardly one bird resembled another, the fully mature cocks being resplendent in much white.

Kestrels remain throughout the winter, though the young disappear in late winter or early spring. From late July onwards, it is usual to see anything up to six or even eight birds hovering in the gulley as they feed on grasshoppers. Sparrowhawks too spend their winter here, as many as four birds being seen together.

Few winters pass without at least one buzzard coming over. In 1970 there were three. In 1977, two were seen from January through until the end of March; they dominated the sky along the South Downs ridge, and many people saw them. One day I heard the garrulous wailing of a crow and knew that it could only mean that a bird of prey was about. Suddenly, a buzzard flapped over the trees less than a hundred feet up, the black barbed crow swinging at him from side to side, as though attached to his tail on a long thread. The buzzard mewed unhappily, unable to outfly the crow whose beak could tap open the head of a young deer. His only defence was to glide away on hot updraughts, and this he attempted, circling back on his track, wobbling unevenly on the weak

BUZZARD

air, flight feathers widely splayed to catch, like extra wings, the smallest help from thermals. But it was not until he reached the warm air of the valley, flowing uphill from the heated, sheltered grassland, that he could attempt to soar higher than the crow. The latter – strong with good feeding and a lazy winter when it was hardly necessary ever to move his wings at anything more than slow rowing pace, to take him from the dung pats of neighbouring pasture back into the reserve – rose time and time again above the moth-like bird, darting at his head with black nutcracker beak. At last the buzzard found the uplift and circled quickly lest it be lost; rising on the narrow column of air shooting invisibly up to several thousand feet, he rode with it, crying 'Wheeoo' again and again, in obvious exhilaration and relief. The crow, too, circled, but his sharper wings, though he splayed them as wide as he might, were not long enough to keep the air current under him; he was left further and further behind as the buzzard was jerked upwards to small cumulus clouds forming over the back of the hills at many thousand feet. The buzzard was soon lost, even in the eye-piece of my binoculars. He was an eyelash, then a speck: soon this wandered in and out of sight, then it was gone, as he went in to the bottom of a cloud. I imagined him then gliding through sun-dazzled, snowy peaks, drifting perhaps with a hoar of ice over his wing edges, his brown mantle grey with the water dust of freezing air. Far below him the crow swooped wearily back to the reserve and flopped into a yew, there to rest.

Tawny owls are resident throughout the year and hoot loudly from October to May, giving away their three territories which have been permanently occupied for at least the past fifteen years. Six owls seems a very low number for such suitable habitat with its enormous vole and mouse population and its great number of hollow trees, but a pair per 50 acres is roughly comparable to the populations of other woodlands that I have known. They are not confined to the yew–ash or yew–oak woodland either, one pair always being present in pure yew wood when the trees are quite small (up to 20 feet) though densely packed. Eric Simms, in *Woodland Birds*, says that tawny owls are rarely recorded in coniferous woodland in Europe, and comments particularly on their being found in yew woodlands. They are also found in mature Douglas fir plantations near my home, where they nest in the platform nests of woodpigeons high up in the crowns (this is because the local broad-leaved trees have few if any suitable holes). Occasionally barn owls are found hunting out the grassland but they never breed here – nor, curiously, do little owls although they are found nearby. I have only once seen a little owl in winter, on a fence post surrounding the reserve.

TAWNY OWL

Perhaps the easiest bird to record is the common pheasant, whose clatter and crowing as it goes up to roost can be heard a mile away. The shooting rights are let to local farmers over parts of the reserve, this being one of the original conditions of sale. The area does not, I suspect, normally hold more than the occasional single bird despite the acorn crop, but during all the time that I have been there several dozen pheasants have been wintering, and about ten are shot each year. Rearing began in 1964, and many of the released birds naturally gravitate into this sheltered, ant-filled valley. But I had been told that prior to this date it was rare to hear a pheasant. The stock varies in its mixture of sub-species, which nowadays are considerably cross-bred. Dark or melanistic birds were introduced in 1968 and this strain occurs still, though not the pale or Bohemian pheasant. Now and again an Old English bird is seen, distinctive with its copper feathers and lack of white collar. Both French and English partridge overwinter here, but in very small numbers despite the abundance of insect food and warm, dry valleys. Woodcock numbers are reinforced by immigrants, and ten birds may be found in the 150-acre valley by January. They fly out at night to feed in the wet cart ruts on nearby farmland, or in frosty weather stay in the reserve to probe the oak-leaf litter for worms or smaller fauna.

One year I found a dead snipe among the old yews. How that came to be there will for ever be a mystery. No other water birds have ever been seen in winter on the reserve, but until very recently (about 1971) the field adjoining our south-eastern boundary was always remarkable for its pair or two of wild duck, which may have had a breeding connection with a small half-filled pond there. But Fred Longman tells me that once, in the 1920s, that field was so filled with mallard that 'you couldn't put a fork down between them without killing one. The noise when they flew up was terrible, and they darkened the whole sky.' The story was verified by other men working there at the time. How many mallard? Even a thousand would be a great number especially in this part of the world, where wildfowl counts for all the harbour from Pagham to Portsmouth are never more than the odd hundred. In the early 1960s I once saw 20 mallard on that field, but within a year or two these had dwindled to the one pair or so.

There was always a curlew there too: in 1963 there was one solitary bird which fed on one corner of the field until precisely 3.40 p.m. when it flew back to Chichester harbour. I think it was the remaining last link with what in the years gone by was a common sight: that of curlews regularly feeding on some slopes of the downs. I am reliably informed by Miss Jessie Carpenter, a resident of Chilgrove, that in the 1920s many curlew bred all over the downs of West Dean – and they were not stone curlews that she was muddling them with for they had beaks 'as long as your hand'. Curlews breeding on the downs! Such an event is unheard of today. What a wealth of wildlife has slipped from us in so short a time – most of it undocumented and forgotten, and now no more than folklore.

The Migrants

There is a continual movement of migrating wildfowl during late winter over the reserve from Chichester harbour to the north-east. Curlews, wigeon and golden plover may be heard, among many more, particularly during March and again in October. On 19 March or a little either side of this date brent geese fly over in flocks of up to 1000 birds, and they go on to pass over my house five miles north-east at about 8.30 p.m. as they start their long journey to their breeding grounds in Siberia. How sad it is to hear winter passing, with Orion the Hunter fading from the southern sky, the grand nights of frost and owl calls in the woods, the breaking-up of the winter deer herds and snow on the hills all giving way to another season of softness and warmth and birdsong.

When the geese have gone the spring migrants appear in force. Wheatears bob with white rumps on the barbed-wire fence posts surrounding local fields, flying ahead of the Landrover for a hundred yards before breaking back to their original posts. Not many are seen, no more than six in any one day along one and a half miles of fencing, but at least their numbers have not declined over the years. Neither have the whinchats, no more than three or four at a time. There was an extra pair, cock and hen, there in late May 1977 though apparently they do not breed in Sussex. Stonechats are always seen but have not overwintered since 1971, though about fifty birds do so in Sussex each year, and about fifty pairs breed as well, though none in the reserve. Then in April redstarts move through in singles or twos, a steady flow in the 1960s, now a very thin trickle of perhaps three or four birds seen altogether. They return again in September from their more northern breeding grounds. Pied flycatchers in even lesser number accompany them, and there is usually one black redstart seen each year.

Once a ring ouzel was watched, looking like a cloaked parson, sitting among the waxy, red yew berries in a green pulpit or bower of yew leaves. One (and occasionally up to three) hoopoe feeds in the reserve for about a week in April, looking more startling in its pink, white and black barred plumage than any other bird. But if visitors see them they usually think they are jays, for they are about the same size. Once a wryneck was seen: in Sussex as a whole, no more than three are seen each spring, though a few more pass out of this county in autumn. By May, there may be a few fieldfares still about, the latest being seen on 6 May, when a singing male stayed in the valley for two days.

Nothing spectacular, you may say, and probably many birds are never recorded, judging by the amount of unusual migrants seen down on the coast, at Beachy Head and Selsey Bill. But these are collecting funnels through which a great number of birds pass before fanning out into the countryside.

The Breeding Bird Community

A mapping method based on that used in the British Trust for Ornithology's Common Bird Census is used for determining the number of breeding territories. During about 12 or 15 separate visits within the period of mid-March to mid-July, the positions of singing males of all species are noted on a map. The positions are then copied on to separate species sheets. Thus, clusters of records for each species show where the males have moved around their territories during this four-month period, and a reasonably accurate picture of the numbers of pairs of birds can be made. Although this has been used from 1963 onwards, only that period from 1967 to 1976 has been analysed in detail, since these are the years which I myself have recorded and for which there is more likelihood of maintaining a standard error/accuracy ratio. An earlier report was published in *British Birds*, No. 66. The survey area covers 143 acres and records five main habitats: chalk grassland, scrub and yew–oak 'islands', young yew wood, middle-aged yew wood and mature yew–ash wood. The census area is the valley and slopes of the reserve's south-facing escarpment, the area generally known as Kingley Bottom, and it is bounded on the slopes by the track now used by the nature trail.

A yew woodland bird community is unusual and so far as I know has not been studied in detail before by the Common Bird Census. It was a year or two before I was able to identify the songs of the 58 species as well as their social and alarm calls. Early on I went to one of the B.T.O. weekend conferences in order to learn something of the methods of recording. An official there gave me a good piece of advice: 'If you hear a call note which you cannot identify, it is probably a great tit – they have at least 90 different calls.' We heard records of marsh and coal tits' songs and calls, and tried to distinguish the differences between blackcap and garden warbler songs. These two I now find quite easy to tell apart, the former being much more of a whistling song with a definite crescendo, whereas the garden warbler makes the lower, churring notes reminiscent of a sedge warbler but on a more expansive scale.

The first bird apparently to start the spring song is the mistle thrush, and each year a pair or two dominate the valley for the month of March, with many more robins and dunnocks around them. But song thrushes may have been singing since December in the frosty gloom, and tawny owls hoot excitedly all through the winter at dusk and at intervals throughout the night. Woodcock begin roding in early February – flying over their territory with their peculiar whistle and grunt and slow wing-flap, two pairs generally being heard in the centre of the valley. Sometimes I have heard them utter the strangest note – more like little owls – and they may fall with spectacular tumbling flight when fighting or courting, almost hitting the ground. The dawn chorus gradually increases, gaining one or two recruits week by week. Chaffinches will begin to sing by mid-January but may cease due to bad weather until early March. Goldcrests may sing on and off all winter through, but are in force from March onwards. Robins break their old winter territories in late February, and the sexes join company instead of competing. Most of them nest low down and many actually on the ground in rough grass or scattered bramble, lining their mossy nests with the shed winter coats of fallow deer.

Despite the attentions of ground predators such as stoat and weasel, most of the nests which I find in the course of my travels seem to bring off their young. The titmice family are well represented and many choose the same old nesting site year after year. Without fail, blue tits have nested by post 5 in the new grove where a branch was once cut off. To check that they are back again each spring, I have, for the past fourteen years, stopped next to the small hole in the trunk, which is at ear level, and every time have been greeted by an explosive hiss in my ear from the brooding bird, deep inside the old yew tree. There is no shortage of nest sites, but even so, a blue or great tit generally avails itself of the glass-backed nesting box let into the museum wall. This is very exciting for the 2000 school children who come to the reserve in May, June and July, for they can watch the young being fed.

Many early nests of such birds as long-tailed tit, mistle thrush and song thrush, dunnock and wren are destroyed by the various corvids and by grey squirrels, and although the gradual decline in total numbers of birds may not be due to them, I still intend to go ahead with the destruction of these predators. The number of sucked pheasant eggs lying around in May shows how the corvids work the area for their livelihood. Anyone who has seen, as I have, a magpie tear to pieces, like someone tearing up an old envelope, a long-tailed tit's nest which has taken a fortnight to build out of lichens, moss, spiders' webs and 2000 feathers and which is crammed with ten half-grown young, will know how destructive the corvids can be.

Other predators on our birds are human ones. Since the film *Kes* there has been a great interest in falconry, particularly in my experience among boys of poorer districts whose own wings are clipped by their environment and who see in falconry a chance to escape momentarily from the dullness of life. This plunder of birds of prey is increasing and is probably going to become serious, especially in nature reserves to which people with little specialised knowledge have easy access. In June 1977 I accosted a young lad of about 18 who drove into the reserve on a new motor-cycle. He was 'checking-up', he told me, on the owls' nests in the reserve. So as to obtain the full story I asked him to lead on, leaving the official business to last. As he led the way unerringly to our three tawny owls' nests, he explained that he and his mates checked up on all the nests of birds of prey in the area for ten miles around, to the north and west. 'Kids come out for the young birds and take 'em home. They feed 'em on bread and 'course they die. Kestrels, owls, the lot. Know what I mean?' This unofficial guardian, *if* that is what he was, checked the nests regularly to 'make sure' the young were still in the nests. The reader may well wonder why the warden does not protect the nests himself? The answer is that he does what he can, but short of defences such as those of the osprey at Loch Garten he is relatively defenceless against so many people, some of whom probably come at night.

No general decline of birds of prey has been shown up by the bird census, although in 1977 there was no brood of young kestrels hunting grasshoppers in the valley in late summer and no sparrowhawk seen regularly in the breeding season for the second year running after their come-back in the late 1960s. Tawny owls, however, have increased. Records of barn owls and little owls were at their greatest when official gamekeeping activities took place at nearby West Stoke Estate. That they are not now seen when the estate is no longer regularly 'keepered' is a coincidence, one presumes. Hobbies do not breed here, but sometimes they swoop into the reserve to catch butterflies. Diving at 80 m.p.h. from five hundred feet they snatch dark green fritillaries just above the grass

140

HOBBY

stems. Climbing again to their pitches they pick the wings off these gaudy insects, which flutter down like spent beech leaves.

The height of the season for me is always May Day morning. By then the nightingales have arrived, and so have most of the other summer residents. Standing in the cold, sometimes frosty centre of Kingley Vale in the dark is like standing and waiting for the dawn in the desert. Nothing can shake off the feeling of desolation and loneliness, yet you know that within minutes that feeling will be gone as daylight comes. There may be the far-away tinkling of a skylark's song, pitched beneath the fading stars, and the nightingales will be hammering out their night-ending sounds down towards the end of the valley. Once, ten years ago, eight nightingales were there, four with territories so close that all four birds were within 15 yards of each other, two on one side of the track, two on the other. No other bird songs could be heard beyond this quarter at dawn. But that has never been repeated, for the birds have gradually declined to two or three pairs.

At 4.30 a.m. a cock pheasant will suddenly go off like a cannon. Others salute him, a chain reaction of waking birds, their thudding wings resounding back and forth. Thirty pigeons awake and at 4.33 a.m., forty robins. Forty blackbirds begin at 4.37 a.m. and within the following minute or so. Soon their song covers every other sound, and recording the positions of other birds becomes impossible. Through this blanket of song, the wheedling of all the titmice begins, some not singing until nearly 5 o'clock. The woodcock flies, unseen above the mist but known by his grunt and whistle, and sometimes the far-off reeling of the nightjar seals the night. I am reminded of the music to Daphnis and Chloë by Ravel, of the dawn of Creation. How can the human spirit fail to respond to such joy? Yet I am alone. Never on May Day have I seen another soul, save once or twice for a friend with me.

The rest of the morning is a quiet, listening walk, silently through cool mossy dells of yews and oaks where the blackcaps sing, along the grass ridge paths of the slopes where orchids are in flower and a tree pipit winds itself up into the sun. In the valley there is a bird to record every few yards, as I walk by; on the slopes one every fifty or more as I reach the young yew woods. Year after year I come to expect the same birds to be singing in each area. There may be more or there may be less, but they are always there. By the end of May some have already begun to go off song. By mid-June there are mainly summer migrants singing continuously, especially whitethroats and blackcaps, and by then the nightingales have finished. Cuckoos sing most a day or two before they cease altogether, and when I cuckoo back they fly and perch overhead and display with great passion in the trees above, waving their fanned tails and making swearing sounds. I have had one male bird follow me out of the reserve until I was beyond its territory and swoop down to my head even though I had stopped the imitation, so angry had it become.

Within a day it can all be over again for another year. Some days are very good for bird song, and if possible everything must be dropped and a census made. These are the days of calm clear weather on a rising barometer, particularly if the weather has been dull and cold beforehand. In June, such a day may be the last for many birds and they

142

will hardly be heard again except at dawn or the odd snatch of song during the morning. But July recording is important since yellow-hammers and corn buntings are in full song then, and turtle doves croon throughout the month. Night visits too must be made for owls, nightjars and grasshopper warblers. When the twelve or more site visits have been made, work begins on copying the details on to separate maps, one for each species. This is hard work, for almost a thousand records have to be dealt with. The species sheets are then assessed by the British Trust for Ornithology, which determines the number of territories that have been held in the reserve. Tables giving detailed analysis of these records may be found in the Appendix.

The Insects

Butterflies

Kingley Vale is perhaps the richest of any of our National Nature Reserves for butterflies, a fact which was not realised until all the reserves started to monitor their populations in 1976. The reason for this is the great range of habitats and foodplants found here, as well as the enviable climate and aspect. Some of the less common species are not very great in number, and they are extremely vulnerable since in some cases only a few plants of the particular host exist. Everything possible is done to conserve these plants.

To show how this is brought into the general management of the yew forest, I shall describe in detail each butterfly and its requirements. It may seem odd that not one butterfly found here could exist on yew trees alone, the prime interest of this reserve, but that all are dependent on the stages of woodland development preceding or following the forest. The reader may be puzzled too as to how the butterflies can be managed or conserved when they are merely a subsidiary part of a secondary interest. But in the foreseeable future it can be done, and it may also be possible to do so in the long term.

First a word about the monitoring technique used to determine the numbers of butterflies and their relative abundance in comparison with other parts of the country. This is known as the Butterfly Monitoring Scheme and was instigated by the Institute of Terrestrial Ecology in 1976. They will publish their own findings from time to time. The aim is to show changes in abundance from year to year and relate these to habitat changes including management, and to other changes. Like the Common Bird Census it serves as a national barometer for one of our more attractive forms of wildlife. It is a fascinating, if at times exhausting, job. Before anyone scoffs at the idea of a man wandering around counting butterflies and then calling it hard work, I would say, try it. My transect is perhaps longer than most, covering about $4\frac{1}{2}$–5 miles, and takes roughly four hours. I do the Common Bird Census at the same time, as both routes are identical (and I pick up litter as well).

Hard work it is – or perhaps was, for surely we will never again see the clouds of butterflies that there were in 1976.

The transect is divided into fifteen sections. Most sections cover different habitats or different management (or both), be it mowing, grazing or just scrub clearance. Each butterfly within a three-yard arc of the walk is recorded in species columns. I began the transect in 1976 knowing that our July butterflies might be dense on hot sultry days, when meadow browns, small heaths and hedge browns were at their peak. Some population studies which we had carried out in the late 1960s on meadow browns showed about 130 insects per day on the plateau, an area of about five acres, and during July and August most of these were replaced within three days by another 130 insects. A meadow brown, it seems, is an old-age pensioner after one week.

At the height of the 1976 season, a transect walked at normal slowish speed (2 m.p.h) on 27 July revealed 914 butterflies of 18 species present along the path. Each one had to be correctly identified, and to facilitate this and the task of counting the numbers accurately I had to resort to a little cunning. Sometimes my route passed a bramble bush, which when in flower attracts numbers of butterflies such as hedge brown. At other times a marjoram clump with its aromatic small purple flowers would lie by the path within the 3-yard arc. If I walked right past at the regulation speed, up to 50 butterflies would be in the air round my head and it would be like counting the pigeons in Trafalgar Square. Instead I would focus my binoculars from a distance of 10 yards and sort out the brown arguses from the female common blues, the hedge browns from the meadow browns, the small coppers from the small skippers. Five hours of this concentration was enough for me in temperatures of 90° F and I was glad to get on with something different for the rest of the day.

The transect is only made in temperatures of 55° F or above. From 55° to 63° F it is made in 60 per cent sunshine or more, and above 63° F the sunshine is not used as a criterion. Weather greatly affects the insects. Pollard *et al.* (1973) showed how sunshine, temperatures and wind subdued or encouraged four species: large skipper, green-veined white, hedge brown and meadow brown. The first doubled its appearance on the transect in favourable as opposed to unfavourable conditions. The second was not affected by the wind and even increased its activity in cloudy weather on some occasions. Hedge browns did not seem to be greatly worried by temperature and wind although they enjoyed sunshine; meadow browns likewise doubled their activity in bright conditions.

As the season progressed I saw that the different species could be

COMMA

MEADOW BROWNS

expected to turn up again and again in the same places. After the summer was over I had more of an idea of their niches by this methodical observation than by my thirteen years of vague watching. And I was more able then to say what could be done within the constraints of management to help each butterfly.

Apart from the results of the transect which I do for the Butterfly Monitoring Scheme, a great deal of work is done by one of the voluntary wardens, Major W. Phillips. An expert on the natural history of Ceylon, now in his eighties, Major Phillips is a regular visitor to the reserve, where he walks the areas not covered by the transect and makes careful and accurate records of everything he sees. Without his expert help much valuable information would be lost, for there is a limit to the amount of time the warden can spend on this sort of work.

Shrub- and Tree-feeding Butterflies

Brimstone   Howarth and South (1973) thought that the brimstone, which was known in 1658, may have introduced the name butterfly to the English language, since it could have been the insect first described as the 'butter-coloured fly'. The male is bright sulphur yellow, the female is greenish yellow. The earliest that I have seen it is in the first week of February, and by April there is a good scattering throughout the reserve, the insects having woken up from winter hibernation. But the numbers which emerge from such a long dangerous sleep in the open are dependent upon the winter weather. If it has been very wet and cold, as in 1976–7, few will be seen. Now and then they are to be found clinging upside down under bramble stems, yew boughs or holly bushes, and during scrub clearing they can sometimes be saved in time and put out of harm's way. One year I found three like this and rather than let them risk the open weather, I sentimentally took them home in a cardboard box and kept them in my shed, returning them to the reserve at the first warm weather when they eventually awoke.

Much more useful to the species is to ensure that it has plenty of buckthorn bushes for the caterpillars to feed upon. Although this shrub is scattered on the reserve it benefits by being completely unpalatable to browsing animals such as deer and donkeys. The female brimstone can be seen in May dancing around a particular twig, and a close watch will show that she is dabbing her abdomen on to the leaves and laying a bright egg. This is clearly visible to the naked eye, and under a hand-lens resembles a ripe corn-on-the-cob. Before many days a camouflaged green caterpillar can be found on shredded leaves. By early August when the pupae hatch a yellow cloud of butterflies may be seen swarming from the eastern spur into the valley; but one is only ever there once in a lifetime to witness the spectacle.

Green hairstreak A butterfly probably never seen by the majority of people, nor even known about, yet once its emerald-green wings have been seen it will never be forgotten. It looks at first like a small leaf torn from a bush in a May gale as it flutters haphazardly amongst the grasses. In May and June it flies in sheltered glades in the valley, having fed on any of a variety of shrubs or herbs. It is reputedly the commonest hairstreak butterfly in Britain because of its wide range of foodplants, yet it is, like all other hairstreaks, relatively uncommon if not rare, and is almost certainly declining. Its particular requirements are not known, except that it almost certainly favours grassy glades in woodland rather than closed canopy – and as long as the chalk glades, scrub and woodland of Kingley Vale remain it is unlikely ever to be at risk in the reserve, except from collectors.

Purple hairstreak This little dark-purple butterfly did not become noticeable until 1976 when it was suddenly quite common in exactly the same areas as the holly blue, that is in the oak woodland of the valley. It emerges in July and August and is not often seen as it flies high around the oak canopy. When emerging, however, it is found dopily wandering with expanding wings among the leaves or herbage beneath the tree where it has pupated. As the oakwood is expanding, so presumably will the purple hairstreak's range.

Holly blue A pretty pale-blue butterfly with black spots, looking like a broken song thrush's egg, the holly blue may be found – in some years in great number – on the main valley path area, imbibing moisture from damp ground. Its best year was 1968, when in April one was to be found every five yards. Since then it has been seen in small numbers, about two insects per day being the average. The two separate broods (April / May and July / August) of caterpillars require separate foodplants. The first, in April, start their feeding career on the flower buds of holly, though I have found them on spindle and they are known to eat dogwood too. But when these young hatch and look for plants on which to lay eggs they invariably choose ivy, whose flowers are very late developers, so the second brood may feed well into the autumn. The ivy is obviously the critical shrub since its distribution exactly matches that of the butterfly in this reserve, whereas spindle and holly are found in many places where the holly blue does not appear. Elsewhere, the insect has been known to decrease as ivy is cleared from forest trees, old buildings and so forth.

White admiral To see this splendid magpie-coloured insect flapping and gliding powerfully along the shaded rides of the oakwood is one of the great occasions of the year. In flight it always reminds me of a manta ray's dark rush through the ocean's depths. No wonder it was originally known as the white admirable. In 1976 it was to be found in no less than five compartments of the valley where previously it was only known in one.

This is another butterfly whose life in the reserve depends on the existence of the small oakwood in the valley, for the eggs are laid on the thin straggling honeysuckles which trail upwards under the oaks. Lush honeysuckle growing in the open among emergent scrub is ignored. After autumn feeding, the larva, which camouflages itself with its own excreta in a caddis-like structure of silk and frass, makes another little hide-out for the winter from the leaf of a honeysuckle drawn together with silk. These can occasionally be found looking like dying leaves attached to honeysuckle stems, but should you find one (or other larvae or caterpillars) please do not disturb it.

Purple emperor This glorious insect with its purple robe and depraved habit of drinking the juice from excreta has in fact only been seen once on the reserve, in the vintage year of 1976. One passed me during the transect walk within the prescribed 3 yards distance and so was recorded. It had the distinction of being the only one recorded on the 34 transects of the Butterfly Monitoring Scheme scattered throughout the British Isles. (Purple emperors have in addition a special survey all to themselves, with observers recording sightings and behaviour in their known or likely haunts.) This one was almost certainly a passer-by from a colony in some nearby oakwoods. It may be a unique sighting for the Vale since so many of the surrounding oakwoods are being destroyed.

The foodplant is not the oak itself, of course, but the sallow willow bushes which often grow in association with old oakwoods. A few of these exist on the reserve and are 'protected', since they are also most useful to queen bumblebees which rely on the rich pollen and nectar-laden catkins in the cold days of March and early April.

Rough Grass-feeding Butterflies, the Browns

Meadow brown This is by far the commonest butterfly each

SPECKLED WOOD

DARK GREEN
FRITILLARY

summer, when its profusion may return one momentarily to the
carefree, halcyon days before the introduction of insecticides, and baffle
the eye with their constant rising from the meadows. The highest count
ever was made on 4 August 1977 when 550 were counted within four
hours. Climatic factors appear to have much greater influence on

number fluctuations than any other single reason, such as differing kinds of management.

Wall brown Looking like a segment of brick wall with black mortar, this butterfly actually owes its name to its desire for the heat reflected from walls and other objects. It is curiously uncommon on the reserve – despite there being plenty of its foodplants, cocksfoot and meadow grasses – and I think this is due to the lack of such south- and particularly west-facing, heat-reflecting objects. Whenever it is seen, it will be on a small overhanging cliff of turf along the tracksides in Cps 1 and 13, basking in colonies of up to ten.

Hedge brown, or gatekeeper, or small meadow brown Easily confused with its near relative the meadow brown, the hedge brown demands special attention during the transect in early August, when great numbers of both are encountered. For instance on 27 July 1976 there were 209 hedge browns and 449 meadow browns. Both butterflies may be found in rough grassland, but the hedge brown clusters around bramble flowers particularly, as well as marjoram and woodsage blossoms. I always feel worried when I cut my grassland in late October, as the little green caterpillars with their brownish heads are then feeding on rough grass; but there are many areas where it can breed apart from the reclaimed grassland.

Speckled wood Like the wall brown, the speckled wood is loyal to one or two areas, though totally different ones, where it may always be found. Thus, although the nature-trail guide was written originally in 1969, when I mentioned that one particular point was a good place to see a speckled wood, people still frequently report that they have seen one in that tiny glade and nowhere else. I almost always pick it up at this point in my transect. The area is a heavily shaded path with a five-foot-wide slit in the canopy of yews. Nearby grasses provide foodplants. It fits exactly into the dappled conditions, with its yellow speckled wings which are the same colours as the fallow deer – the 'pied beauty' immortalised by Gerard Manley Hopkins.

Marbled white Common to the east of the reserve on the East Sussex Downs, and to the west in Dorset, this 'magpie' insect, once called 'Our Half-Mourner' because of its half black colour, only just occurs here. How the occasional sightings are maintained is a puzzle, because if it can be seen once every four years there must be a breeding stock

151

somewhere on the reserve, albeit a very small one and confined to the unlikely area of the valley floor in Cp. 1. Never more than three are seen in these well-spaced years. There is the chance that the butterflies have been blown here from far away, but if so it is odd that they always turn up in the same place. There is no shortage of their foodplant of various kinds of grass.

Small heath From mid-May to its peak in late June (202 were recorded on 24 June 1976) the small heath dominates the butterfly population, when it is overtaken by meadow browns. It continues in decreasing numbers until the end of September. It is well scattered on all the same open grassland areas as the meadow brown. It is easy to distinguish on the wing from all the other tiny butterflies such as brown argus, small copper and female blues because of its very slow lazy flight. Eggs are laid on fine grasses, but it obviously benefits from shelter as its greatest numbers, as with the meadow brown, are found in Cp. 8.

Ringlet This slow-flying butterfly has sooty-brown wings like velvet, with small white, black and yellow roundels like eyes on the wing margins. It is found in heavily wooded glades all over the valley.

Small skipper and large skipper These belong to the *Hesperiidae*, and are both rough grassland feeders when in the larval stage. They present no conservation problems as they are more or less confined to the very rough areas. These foxy-red insects dart powerfully along the rides and are so small that they are scarcely seen. However, when at rest they are confiding. The highest count of the small skipper was 85 in mid-July 1976, and of the large, 28 in mid-June.

Essex skipper This has only very recently been established as existing within the reserve, although it has probably been here for a long time. The fact that it is so like the small skipper makes it almost impossible to separate from that species on the transect, for each insect would have to be caught to find out whether or not it had the black tips to the undersides of the antennae. It is only in comparatively recent years that additional colonies to those in the Essex marshes have been found as far west as Salisbury Plain.

Nettle Feeders
Peacock, red admiral, small tortoiseshell, comma None of these common butterflies are at all well represented on the reserve, and

it would be a little unusual if they were. Nettles, after all, have little place on a chalk grassland reserve. But grassland management has provided little pockets of nettles, which is all to the good. The cut grass, dumped in the same piles every year behind trees and in other out of the way places, grows nettles, and it is on these that the caterpillars feed. Peak counts from selected dates in 1976 or 1977 are peacock, 20; red admiral, 6; small tortoiseshell, 19; comma, 10.

For some unknown reason 1975 was a quite remarkable year for red admirals, not just on the reserve but all over Britain. I counted 56 butterflies on the trunk of one oak tree, where a wound produced fermenting sap. The admirals were drunk and could be picked up on the finger after they had imbibed for half an hour.

Violet Feeders

Dark green fritillary The dark green is the commonest fritillary, and at times old-fashioned 'clouds' of this fine orange insect may be seen flying rapidly up and down the plateau and slopes of the reserve. Some entomologists have thought that Kingley Vale is probably the best place in Britain to see it. The peak count has been 44 on the transect on 7 July 1976. In the same week the following year only 15 were seen, the peak for 1977. I have known better years though, notably 1974 when they were to be seen in many farmland hedgerows scattered around the reserve – one thistle plant had 35 insects feeding from its freshly opened flowers. It has undoubtedly benefited from our grassland cutting, which has produced a great increase in dog violets on the plateau meadows; the same result was experienced in the turf of the main paddock after grazing by ponies.

High brown fritillary The high brown fritillary is found only occasionally, but since identification is so difficult some may be missed. It is more of a woodland species than the dark green, and it is hard to see why its range is so small on the reserve, since woodland glades with violets abound on the plateau.

Pearl-bordered and small pearl-bordered fritillaries Since the pearl-bordered emerges first, in May and June, this is one of the easiest ways to separate it from the small, as they are both very similar in appearance. Numbers are never high, with maximum counts of 4 for the first, and 8 for the second. Their strongholds, however, are the small well-sheltered glades on the plateau where fragments of chalk heath vegetation exist, away from the transect.

Vetch Feeders

Common blue The blues represent the spirit of the downs, and for many people are the loveliest sight of the area. Because they are selective in their feeding habits and their particular food is less abundant they tend to be declining in number. However, at Kingley Vale bird's-foot trefoil abounds in the turf, and is increasing due to grazing and cutting, so one would expect the good numbers of this, the commonest blue, to continue here. There are two distinct broods. In 1976 a transect figure of 60 was maintained for late May and the whole of June with a peak of 73, and four weeks in mid-July to mid-August gave the same figures. In 1977 the figures were quartered due to bad weather. Past experience shows that the usual figures are slightly less than those for 1976.

Although the foodplant is essential and it only flourishes in a short sward, the common blue also seems to require long grass near at hand on which to rest. Largest numbers of the butterfly are found where both conditions exist, and this reinforces the view that butterflies, if not meadow insects in general, do require a range of grass types. Fortunately, we are able to provide these conditions by cutting late in the season, grazing only periodically, and leaving other areas untouched on the margins of the meadowlands.

Adonis blue The adonis blue has been recorded on the reserve, but very infrequently, which is partly due to the general lack of its foodplant, the horseshoe vetch. This is surely the most beautiful of all our small butterflies with its electric-blue wings, a colour sometimes seen in azure summer air.

Chalkhill blue One distinct colony of chalkhill blues lives in one small glade cleared especially for it. This is where the horsehoe vetch abounds over several square yards of turf, and were it not for management, this downland turf would long ago have vanished under bramble, birch, and oak seedlings. When the pale blue butterflies emerge, many feed continuously on one small clump of marjoram flowers by the side of their nursery, and up to 50 butterflies are to be found, sucking the nectar of the aromatic flowers. Others scatter from their glade and are found within half a mile in odd corners of the reserve. However, in 1977 my friend Michael Bennett, who looked after the reserve while I was on holiday, found a second colony on the opposite side of the valley, and a close watch will be kept there in future.

Dingy skipper Looking more like a brown moth, this skipper is

154

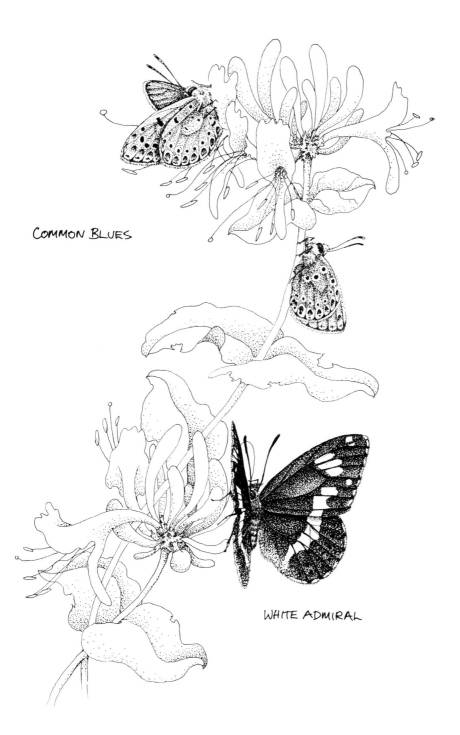

COMMON BLUES

WHITE ADMIRAL

another insect dependent on bird's-foot trefoil but is not quite as frequent as the common blue, the maximum count on 24 May 1976 being 57.

Rock Rose Feeder
Brown argus   The brown argus is a blue, but shows no trace of such colour except perhaps for the vaguest tinge of purple over its sooty wings inside the rows of orange dots. It has a few distinct colonies over small patches of downland turf where the rock rose grows, and as the transect runs through such a place it is often recorded in Cp. 5, the highest count being 16 at the end of August 1976. Rock rose, better known to gardeners in its cultivated forms of *Helianthenum*, is not a difficult plant to keep going in the wild provided that hot, dry, south-facing slopes with ant-heaps, where the low creeping runners can colonise, are protected from trampling and from invading rough grasses and shrubs.

Primula Feeder
Duke of Burgundy fritillary   The Duke of Burgundy is not related to the other fritillaries, but is a metalmark and the only European representative of this largely American family. It is a small insect with black and orange chequered wings. It is found in only one corner of the reserve, a nook surrounded by dense shelter of slopes and trees, and is dependent on a few plants of primrose upon which it feeds and under which it hides. Its existence is precarious, but fortunately the area is inaccessible and so the plants are safe from picking. Some scrub and bramble is cleared back from time to time to maintain this small area of rich downland turf.

Sorrel Feeder
Small copper   The small copper is one of the most exquisite of butterflies: a fresh insect is a rich lustrous copper colour, set off by black spots. With its miniature size and tremendous agility and speed it is sometimes difficult to see, and may be missed altogether as it whizzes along the hot sunny track. It is always present on the transect, with peaks at the end of May (maximum 30) and the end of July (maximum 47). There is no shortage of its foodplant but it seems to prefer the proximity of long untouched grassland, as does the common blue.

Cinquefoil and Raspberry Feeder
Grizzled skipper   The grizzled skipper is a minute dark-brown

butterfly with yellow dots; its fast flight makes it look somewhat like a fly. It comes with the spring, and has gone by mid-summer. The maximum count was 40 on 27 May 1977, and it was found throughout almost all sections of the reserve, the exception being the densely shaded areas under the yews in Cps 2 and 3. However, it does not like open meadows. Its foodplant is provided by raspberry canes, cinquefoil, tormentil, and barren strawberry plants, all of which live in distinct and widely separated groups, the last two being well provided for under our management programme.

Lady's Smock Feeder
Orange tip   The orange tip is very scarce – 6 only being seen in 1977– because only one of its foodplants occurs on the reserve, and that only in small amounts.

Mignonette Feeder
The large white, small white and green-veined white   The commonest of these is the small white, with a maximum count of 49, as opposed to 10 for the large and 2 for the green-veined.

Moths

In 1976 a permit was granted for research on the night-flying moths. By means of a portable generator a bright light was set up, with sheets below on which to identify the insects. Three nights of light trapping produced good swarms of moths, with up to 100 species being recorded altogether. It is hoped to continue the work; it was most interesting to be able to examine so many species under controlled conditions. Notable moths include the elephant and small elephant moths with their elegant pink and grey suits, like ladies at Ascot; humming bird hawk, and privet hawk, broad-bordered and narrow-bordered bee hawk, with their hovering action which seems out of place in Britain and reminds one of tropical islands.

An attempt to provide for the requirements of every moth is a daunting one, and should not in fact really be contemplated, even if their various requirements were known. The reserve is obviously very rich and diverse in habitat, and the balance of grass–scrub woodland is as beneficial to this group of insects as it is to butterflies and birds.

(*Note*: A detailed list of the moths and butterflies recorded may be found in the Appendix.)

LEOPARD MOTH

ELEPHANT
HAWKMOTH

Other Insects

Hymenoptera

Members of the bee family are legion, and all have the most fascinating
life-histories. These are a study in themselves, and one in which I have
only minimal knowledge.

One bee in particular that has been noticed on Kingley Vale is *Ceratina cyanea* (Kirby), which is thought to be rare and caused much interest when it was discovered here by a member of the British Museum's Natural History department, Mr G. Else. He found that the bee nested in dead, soft-pitched stems with clean broken ends, e.g. bramble, rose and mulleins. The female excavated the pith to produce a linear gallery; the individual cells in each nest were separated from each other by partitions made from pith. Juvenile bees of both sexes overwintered in these partitions. Else found that the bee did not occupy stems down in the valley which seemed suitable, but only those in the south-facing suntrap and gulley of the main grazing paddock. Quite a bit of scrub clearing had taken place here, and some of the bramble was never burned but was piled up and thrust into another bush which was not to be cut. This was purely fortuitous for the bee – though at the back of my mind, as in practically everything I do, was the thought, 'Don't throw it away – it might be useful'. It was, and now odd bits of bramble when snipped off to clear paths are left there. In nature, the cliché holds: there is a place for everything, and everything in its place. The balance is held by a force that is greater than man.

Beetles

The visitor, even if *he* be unobservant, can't fail to notice the beetles in spring, whereas *she* may be alarmed if she is not used to such things. Large black-blue beetles crawl ponderously over the turf, traversing everything in their way. If they are picked up these beetles will exude a reddish brown evil-smelling liquid from their mouths, hence the name, bloody-nosed beetle.

Many of the other small and large beetles on the reserve have not yet been identified. One or two crawl to mind, however, particularly the ferocious tiger beetle. What a fellow he is! As soon as the light is of a certain intensity (and my eye recognises the time of year unaided by a calendar) he is there, on a particular stretch of path in Cp. 5. I know before I start off up the path that I will see the bright green creature. He is slim, remarkably energetic, completely single-minded. At first he flies in short spurts ahead of me. I stop and crouch, selecting a pebble of chalk from the ground, flicking it in his direction. He changes his whole aspect. Turning, he gallops towards me and seizes the pebble! He thinks it is a fly. Time after time I toss them past his ear, and whichever way they go he turns and gives chase. We play this game for ten minutes or so, he reminding me of a Sicilian bandit in a green cloak. Sometimes I find him in the winter in his deep chalk tunnel burrowed a foot into the

ROMAN SNAIL &
TIGER BEETLE

ground, a larvae with huge jaws who will spring out like a Jack-in-the-box to snatch his prey that is wandering harmlessly by.

The ugly oil beetle that crawls like a bloated cockroach over the spring grasses is now quite rare. Finding one for the first time as recently as 1976, I was dismayed to discover that its foodplant as an adult is privet. In the place where I found it the donkeys had eaten all the privet bushes – a fact in which I had been rejoicing, since the bushes were swamping chalk grassland. I consoled myself with the thought that there was plenty of privet elsewhere. Who would not do all they could to protect such an extraordinary creature? The female, who looks as though she is heaving 14 tons of coal about on her back, is in fact pregnant with many thousands of eggs. She lays them in cracks in the ground, some dug by herself. They hatch into tiny 'lice' which swarm over flowers, awaiting the visits of bees. Eventually, some may be lucky and hook themselves into the fur of a bee – if they are unlucky enough to meet a fly or any other insect they will perish, for what they want is honey. Riding everywhere with the bee like Toad in his motor car, they arrive at her nest. They wait until she has constructed the brood chamber and, as she lays her egg, one of them will slide down her abdomen and drop into the cell with the egg. The bee seals up the cell, little thinking that anything is wrong. But inside, the larva rips open the egg and eats it. Now, as a hairy 'louse' it would quickly drown in the sticky honey, so it moults into a new shape–one which has been described as having 'a pair of paddle-shaped jaws to push the honey into its mouth, a smooth body which will float, with enough freeboard to keep the breathing holes above the entangling honey and scarcely any legs'. It moults into different shapes to accommodate its new life when the honey is all gone, and finally emerges as a beetle.

There is room to mention only one more beetle, the glowworm, which is still found on the downs. My wife and I spend a late evening counting them on the reserve each June or July, when the weather is calm and warm and the pale summer stars don't vie with the strange, somewhat eerie, greenish light emanating from the grasses. Our record count was in 1976, when we saw 21 females glowing in the turf at various places scattered throughout the grassland. Last year, I was worried to find three of their juvenile larvae inside a coke tin that had been thrown away. Luckily they seemed to have only just got inside, for certainly they could not have got out of the slippery sides of that metal prison. They were feasting on a pair of snails which had also crawled into the pseudo shelter, and I wondered how many others had perished in this way, through a moment's carelessness from the throw-away generation.

What It's All About

Education

Our interpreting service began in 1966 with National Nature Week. I wrote the text for a nature trail and my wife spent laborious hours hand-printing it all on to separate boards, complete with maps and drawings, which I attached to posts and set up around the footpaths. There were stories about witchcraft in the grove, a history of the yews, paragraphs on chalk grassland and whitethroat warblers, on redwings and fieldfares from Russia spreading yew berries, on roe deer browsing dogwood and bee orchids needing six years to germinate. We put all the notices up and they stood silently in the dusk, like headhunters waiting for the public.

But in the daylight the next morning it was obvious that all these varnished notices were out of place on the green hills. They were kept up for the week and about 400 people seemed to read and enjoy it all, although there were rude remarks from a minority on the backs of some of the boards. One American, at least, was impressed; he sought out my wife (sitting patiently handing out leaflets about Nature Week, rather obviously pregnant, with a small infant playing in the mud at her feet) and gave her half-a-crown 'to buy the young lad a book'!

For the same occasion I set up an exhibition in Chichester Museum, of downland and harbour wildlife. My wife and I sat up for many nights making a papier-mâché model of Kingley Vale out of 30 copies of the *Sunday Times* and covering it with make-believe chalk turf, chalk heath, beech and pine forest in convincing miniature. For yew trees we picked off the yew galls which are formed by the branch tips when the gall midge *Cecidomya taxi* lays her eggs in the spring. The galls resemble tiny yew trees and are about a centimetre tall. The model had been on display in the museum for about three days when the Curator phoned to ask why she had suddenly been plagued with a swarm of tiny flies. I went down and found hundreds of adult gall midges hatching out of all my model yew trees and covering the windows in their attempts to get outside.

My boarded nature trail was printed into booklet form and has now gone through several editions of increasing sophistication until the present form, in colour, was printed in 1977. About 4000 are sold each year. The text covers all the main habitats and the animals and birds which have a particular relationship with them.

I thought that to make it easier for parents at the weekend, lumbered with children in spring mud or summer heat, a question and answer technique would help entice the less interested kids up the steep 400-foot climb. Each short paragraph, therefore, leads up to a question; and summer after summer I pass by, to hear the same hesitant answers being volunteered at the same places in the depth of the grove by unseen trail followers, and I listen and know that it is good.

The small field museum was more ambitious. It was the logical extension of my own personality, for since early childhood I had been unable to discard any feather, skull, pellet or bone found during my country rambles. So it was a pleasure to fill the small octagonal cedar-wood building (designed by our Buildings and Maintenance Officer, Mr Ivor Owen, and opened in 1969) with animals and birds which I had found dead on the roads and which were still in perfect condition. The idea of keeping road casualties had begun when the Conservancy staff were asked to keep records, for a survey, of the numbers of road victims seen on our travels to work. The number of deaths over a short mileage during the course of one year was amazing. Specimens were, at first, skinned and preserved and mounted on cards. The skull was also attached to the card, and details of the animal's weight, measurements and the cause of death were added. This detailed work was carried out by Major Bill Phillips, previously mentioned.

Then I heard about the method of preserving carcasses with formalin. It sounded easy – too easy – but there were few snags. A mouse, for instance, could be injected with 5 millilitres of formalin in seconds and it would be preserved in that state for ever more. However, the specimens continue to dry for several years and in that time can change shape – the head, particularly, turning in an unnatural direction. That is a small matter when children, and often adults too, can pick up and examine the real thing perhaps for the first time.

After preserving some moles, yellow-necked mice, stoats and weasels, and many small passerine birds I began on bigger specimens. The three-day-old roe kid killed by a dog was preserved with about 20 injections. It remains the most popular exhibit and has been photographed dozens of times by school children. A barn owl was picked up one night in Chichester after it had bounced off the windscreen of a lorry; another was found drowned in a water-butt. Two tawny owls came to hand, and three kestrels were found dead in three successive August weeks – a bad time for the young ones who find it difficult to adapt to feeding themselves.

Some bizarre deaths include a sparrowhawk which hit a church window, a lesser spotted woodpecker which was killed by a dog on a post and rail fence, and a greater spotted woodpecker which was found speared to death on a sharp twig 20 feet above the ground. A water vole was swallowed and then regurgitated by a heron. Another heron died after being a family pet for several years; this is a magnificent bird with a full plume on the head and broad grey vanes which dominate the airspace of the museum.

A pair of hedgehogs which I injected are particularly useful for introducing town children to the feel of their prickles. One is a baby with soft prickles – the girls often manage to overcome their fear of this, and some of the braver ones will progress to holding the adult in their bare hands.

The only failure that I have had was a fox whose tail slipped in hot weather. This was a young vixen in milk which died in a snare, and as it was found the morning before we left for Devon on holiday, it had to be taken with us in the boot of the car, for which my family were not forgiving.

I must point out that formalin can be dangerous, and I do this work in a shed put by specially for the purpose; great care and the use of good gloves is essential, for spilt formalin on the skin could result in the nerve endings being affected, and loss of the use of a hand. All specimens are left to dry out for a long time before being transferred to the museum.

Great is the interest shown in the adder pickled in alcohol. After the roe kid, it is the first to draw every child's eye. Every child too, will ask 'Is it live?' knowing that it cannot be, its head submerged, its quiescent coils moving gently only when the jar is moved. But the black zigzag is enough to strike fear into the spine, and they want assurance that it will not slither out of its twelve-year prison on the very day that they come to the reserve. I tell them that all adders are frightened, with a fragile backbone easily broken if stepped upon; that they bite only if suddenly disturbed or stood on.

I have found a good way to teach children about litter. Many of them shut off when asked not to drop litter. It is part of the adult 'don't do this, don't do that' patter that has become meaningless with repetition. I have a coke tin, with a pygmy shrew, and the diminutive body which can so easily slip inside the pear-shaped opening. I demonstrate putting in the shrew head-first. 'When you have gone home and are sitting comfortably by the telly, out here, in the damp dew grass, the mice and shrews come out to look for food, which they find by sniffing around. One thing they may smell is the drink tin that you've thrown away. They climb up the grasses and smell the sugary sweetness, look inside the opening, drop in and drink. And they can never, never get back out, because they are in a huge metal prison.'

With the next prop to hand, a bottle with skeletons of mice inside (I once found one with 37 skulls, but unfortunately did not keep it), I rattle the bones, and point to the foodchain chart on the wall which shows how voles and mice are often the staple diet of many mammals and birds. No small mice: therefore, no tawny owls. At the end of the visit, the children will have dragged one or two old rusty cans out of the undergrowth and left them on the museum steps for me as a token of their care.

In order to bring live and moving creatures into the museum, a nest box was let into the wall, and a glass back fitted, through which children could watch young great tits and once, blue tits, being fed by the parent birds when the wooden cover was removed from the glass. In 1976 a tree wasp built her nest in the box and a splendid grey paper cricket-ball began to grow, with the workers crawling over it feverishly examining, mending, and adding to the pillars, roof, and walls, looking like a bee-line of taxis in a multi-storey car park. In the winter a great tit hacked the nest to shreds and slept on the debris at night.

An ingenious ants' nest was made by our Assistant Regional Officer, David Harvey, out of plaster of Paris and contained in a small neat box with a glass top, and a wooden flap to cover it. By lifting the flap, the visitor can see common yellow hill ants feeding and tending the queen's eggs in special galleries. Eventually these queens hatch out and mate with the much smaller male flying ants.

In 1969, between May when the museum was first opened and October, when the 'season' virtually ends, 4000 visitors and 700 school children had passed through. (Further details of the numbers of visitors over the years may be found in the Appendix, p. 204.) The museum is open to the general public at weekends only, according to the weather. Even this is very time-consuming because someone, myself or a voluntary helper, has to be on duty, and it is not therefore possible for that person to patrol the reserve, to look out for the many minor transgressions that occur – litter being dropped, flowers picked, the occasional car braving the ruts – and to guard against the perennial fear, that of a fire being started. So you can see that the small band of

165

voluntary workers, who give so freely of time and effort, are a very necessary part of the scene.

Schools can make appointments during the week, and the museum is opened specially for them. I talk to the children for a short while, and they spend what time they want in the museum; then they go off on the nature trail while I get on with the other work that makes up the daily round. The schools come not just from the local area but from many miles around. For instance, Butlin's at nearby Bognor run an Educational Fortnight, and we have visits from schools from all over the country who are staying there. At least 300 immigrant children from the east and south suburbs of London visit the reserve each year, as part of a week-long holiday in Sussex organised by the local College of Education.

Many of the classes that visit the reserve do some follow-up work when they return to school. Some of the schools forward this to me, and one panel inside the museum is reserved for their work: collages of woodland scenes and attendant birds and mammals, books of their visits, with photographs, drawings and text on specific subjects are displayed. As new work arrives it takes its place and older stuff is removed. The children take great pride in bringing Mum and Dad back at the weekends, to see their work on show. In identifying with the reserve, and so with nature as a whole, one hopes that they are more likely to respect and care for it when they grow up.

Conclusion

The fascination of a warden's job is a combination of its creativity, its variety, and the utter conviction that it is worth while. I suspect that some of the visitors to the reserve at the weekends, who see me only when I am sitting in the museum, catching up with office work at the same time, think that my job is a sinecure. It is a grand job, and I wouldn't do anything else, but it is also a difficult job, demanding of time and energy.

A warden should be able to recognise all the forms of wildlife on his reserve and make at the very least records, and if possible distribution maps, of them all, at best carry out some form of scientific research. Birds, mammals, trees, plants and the larger insects are reasonably easy to come to terms with, but there are the minutiae, many of which can only be left to experts who work in a very narrow field. One is always learning, there is always something new to wonder at.

I have had to learn about museum displays and internal combustion engines, public relations, wildlife legislation, management of grazing stock (ponies, donkeys and sheep), and a hundred details of estate management. I have had to maintain a reasonable level of physical fitness to carry them all out, too. Fencing the pony paddock, for instance, involved carrying the fence posts and rolls of barbed wire up the hillside of the Vale at its steepest part, and banging each separate post in with a 56 pound drive-all, which has to be lifted up and down above or at shoulder height, whether in pouring rain or blazing sunshine.

Dealing with the public needs other qualities. I remember arriving one summer morning, some years ago now, to find three dozen cream buns tied to the yew trees, dangling succulently like tropical fruit. Beyond them, on the hilltop, was a table set with a white cloth, a cake, and a carving-knife. Nobody was to be seen there. The cloth moved idly in the breeze. Skylarks sang overhead, meadow pipits rose and fell with opened wings, trilling quietly. Was I still asleep in my cottage? Time passed. Three lovely girls with flowing hair approached, then more; at length young men came too, and they looked on the feast with wonder and laughed. They cut down the buns and ate the cake. I had to break the spell, the surrealist scene, by duty. It was the College of Education, and the tutors had staged the show as a kind of initiation ceremony designed to break down barriers before the serious work began. Later that year the students returned, as others do every year, to record transects across the grassland in order to monitor changes due to grazing, part of their training in environmental sciences.

There are many other things that go to make up the warden's day, his week, his month, his year. There are the local societies and clubs who want me to lecture about my work. There are the brown envelopes full of reports and articles which have to be read in order to keep up with the national, and international conservation scene. The telephone often rings in the evenings (when people know I am *most* likely to be at home) with queries as diverse as the woman who had found parrots in her garden, the farmer who wanted to replace dying elms with native species, and the child who had found a baby deer and unwisely brought it home. Others ask for information regarding jobs in the conservation field, for identification of plants, birds and insects. The list is endless. My wife tries to take the brunt of this, but there are many details that I have to answer myself. On occasions I act in an advisory role for other organisations, for that is one of the main *raisons d'être* of the Nature Conservancy Council. I keep an official eye on Chichester harbour, and because of work I had done on the brent geese which gather there in the winter, I once represented the Nature Conservancy at a public inquiry in Kent, when the hovercraft service to the continent was being conceived.

The purpose of this book is to describe the intricate workings of just over half a square mile of British countryside. It has taken me fifteen years to get to know it intimately: I hope that the reader will tread softly when he goes to this quiet place, that he will be aware of the minute detail of all the creatures and plants that strive for their place in the sun. Left to itself, and to the public, Kingley Vale would by now have been filled with litter, its open glades an impenetrable tangle, many of its rarer butterflies and plants declining, while our knowledge of the world we live in would be the poorer.

But Kingley Vale is just one of many such places in Britain, 735 of which are described in the Nature Conservancy Council's 'Doomsday Book' *The Nature Conservation Review*, which are irreplaceable. Some of the other 734 sites have wardens with the same or greater skills of management and scientific inquiry as myself, and others are cared for by such bodies as the National Trust, the Forestry Commission, the Royal Society for the Protection of Birds, the Trusts for Nature Conservation, and the many other organisations that care for and protect the land, with a great sense of their responsibility towards wildlife conservation.

There are thousands of other places too, such as the Sites of Special Scientific Interest (SSSI) – the official designation to draw attention to an area which has a particular habitat, or contains a particular species, often its last stronghold. Protection for these areas is more difficult; planning control is quite strong, but legislation is particularly weak outside development control issues, for example agricultural reclamation, drainage, land 'improvement' and so on.

The pity is that the potential for looking after such worthy causes as the bog plants of Norfolk, the mountain flowers of Wales or the bats of Devon is there. Each week someone rings up my house to ask how they can get into the Nature Conservancy Council or a similar job. Each advertised warden's post has queues of excellent and suitable applicants, whose dream has always been to work with animals, look after flowers, patrol mountains, to protect and care for and improve a piece of countryside; all of whom, bar one, will have to be turned down.

Under the government-sponsored Job Creation Scheme this situation has to a small extent been relieved, and some good work is being carried out by students on short-term contracts. There is a great deal of work still to be done. Little tern's eggs are being crushed by holiday visitors or stolen by unscrupulous dealers, when one more man at a colony could

168

save them; orchids are still being bulldozed in to make way for buildings; saltings are still being destroyed by people who have grown old with the idea that immediate profit is all.

It is extraordinary to me as a naturalist (but not as a journalist) that we can shed a tear at the death of a panda or a giraffe, but not bat an eyelid at the destruction of a thousand moths, a hundred butterflies, fifty birds, when just one acre of oak woodland is cleared. There are of course people who care, and I should like to pay tribute to those who put time and effort into conservation, without thought of any reward. Some of them labour literally night and day on such tasks as protecting the osprey nests or guarding a rare orchid site.

One day we will be in the happy state of knowing the requirements and position by grid reference of all our fauna and flora, but this will be partly because we have so reduced them that the task is at last possible. How jealously we will guard them then, bewailing the folly of our forebears who threw them away. We will realise that kestrels are just as important to the man on the pavement as they are to the birdwatcher, for the one needs the bird of prey as an indicator of the health of the world just as the other does for his own spiritual health. If animals such as hawks, at the end of complicated foodchains, die so quickly when certain pesticides are used they are as useful to the human race as the canaries down coalmines which once warned miners of deadly gas. We would now be sick with organo-chloride poisons if the birds had not died first in the 1960s.

Gradually awareness increases, but will it be in time? In a now famous illustration of man's place in the universe a clock is drawn – the ages represent the hours, from the dim prehistoric past to the present day. Man enters at three minutes to midnight. Let us hope that the clock is not going to stop on the hour.

Awareness is increasing; every book, every article, every lecture, every mention of conservation helps. One should never be depressed by the odds. When I turn out on a cold winter evening to give a lecture, my audience may be only a few elderly people. Never mind – one of them may be the wife of a well-to-do farmer who is about to reclaim a meadow where the green-veined orchid grows, another may be the chairman of a parish council whose members are in two minds as to whether a bluebell wood should be saved. Optimism may be groundless but I never admit it. For years I have enthused about the rare brent geese which are found here in our harbours on the south coast, and which migrate back to Russia in the spring. Now the harbours are managed with great care and skill so that the geese are not disturbed. Now the Russians have declared reserves for them on the Siberian coast, where previously they had been slaughtered as they sat, flightless in summer moult, at their nests. So I know that however small my contribution might be, the ripples will spread to increase man's understanding of his world.

Bigger ripples are created by the many battles fought by the dedicated team in the N.C.C. and other conservation bodies. The tenacity of one man in saving certain water-meadows not a hundred miles from London; the diplomacy and resourcefulness of another in securing for the nation one of the finest stretches of downland turf where adonis blue butterflies dance in their thousands; the home-work, at the expense of home-life, put in by a third to save a certain estuary: these are the success stories. These men have developed skills by their own effort, with only the briefest groundings for the complicated range of problems they must deal with. They have to face the battleguns of big business, where the ammunition is money – and often, because the national balance sheets are at stake, they lose. But increasingly they are respected, increasingly their views are sought.

There is a long way to go. One day no doubt computers will tell us the value of an orchid versus an air terminal; as yet the man in the Nature Conservancy Council office has to supply the evidence and persuade the powers-that-be that the orchid must win. And it is on your behalf that they fight, yours, and your children, and their children, down to the last generation.

Appendix

Measurements of yew trees at Kingley Vale

circumference of largest trees 1977			diameter/known age (in Loudon, Arb. Brit.) 1838		
ft	in	metres	ft	in	years
20	4	6.20	3	0	200
18	1	5.53	3	0	89
17	10	5.43	2	8	134
17	4	5.28	2	6	200
17	0	5.18	2	5	187
16	9	5.10	2	0	140
16	1	4.90	2	0	45
15	8	4.78	1	8	35
15	1	4.60	1	8	120
15	0	4.57	1	0	70

List of snails found to date at Kingley Vale

Woodland snails

Clausilia bidentata
Clausilia rolphi
Marpersa laminata
Ena obscura
Discus rotundatus
Retinella nitidula
Oxychilus sp.
Oxychilus alliarius
Pomatius elegans
Helicigona lapicida
Cepaea hortensis
Helix asperisa

Grassland snails

Helicalla vingata
Hellicalla itala
Helicalla caperata
Hygromia hispida
Cochlicopa lubrica
Retinella pura
Retinella radiatula
Vitrea contracta
Cepaea nemoralis

List of plants found at Kingley Vale

(*It is not suggested that this list is exhaustive*)

Acer campestre	Field maple
Achillea millefolium	Yarrow
Adoxa moschatellina	Moschatel
Agrimonia eupatoria	Agrimony
Agrostis stolonifera	White bent grass
Ajuga reptans	Bugle
Anagallis arvensis	Scarlet pimpernel
Anthoxanthum odoratum	Sweet vernal grass
Anthriscus sylvestris	Cow parsley

Anthyllis vulneraria	Kidney vetch
Arctium minus	Burdock
Arenaria leptoclados	Small thyme-leaved sandwort
Arenaria serpyllifolia	Thyme-leaved sandwort
Arrhenatherum elatius	False oat (grass)
Asperula cynanchica	Squinancy wort
Atropa bella-donna	Deadly nightshade
Bellis perenis	Daisy
Betula verrucosa	Silver birch
Brachypodium sylvaticum	Slender false brome (grass)
Briza media	Quaking grass
Bryonia dioica	White bryony
Calluna vulgaris	Ling
Campanula glomerata	Clustered bellflower
Campanula rotundifolia	Harebell
Capsella bursa-pastoris	Shepherd's purse
Carduus crispus (acanthoides)	Welted thistle
Carduus nutans	Musk thistle
Carex caryophyllea	Spring sedge
Carex flacca	Glaucous sedge
Carlina vulgaris	Carline thistle
Carpinus betulus	Hornbeam
Catapodium rigidum	Fern grass
Centaurea nemoralis	Brown knapweed
Centaurea nigra	Hardhead (lesser knapweed)
Centaurea scabiosa	Great knapweed
Centaurium erythraea (minus)	Common centaury
Cephalanthera damasonium	Large white helleborine
Cerastium glomeratum	Sticky mouse ear
Cerastium vulgatum	Mouse-ear chickweed
Chamaenerion angustifolium	Rose bay willowherb
Cirsium acaulon	Dwarf thistle
Cirsium arvense	Creeping thistle
Cirsium palustre	Marsh thistle
Cirsium vulgare	Spear thistle
Clematis vitalba	Traveller's joy (Old man's beard)
Clinopodium vulgare	Wild basil
Coeloglossum viride	Frog orchid
Cornus sanguinea	Dogwood
Crataegus monogyna	Hawthorn
Crepis capillaris	Smooth hawk's beard
Dactylis glomerata	Cocksfoot grass
Daucus carota	Wild carrot

Digitalis purpurea	Foxglove
Dryopteris filix-mas	Male fern
Epilobium montanum	Broad-leaved willow herb
Erica cinerea	Bell heather
Euonymovs europaeus	Spindle
Eupatorium cannabinum	Hemp agrimony
Euphrasia officinalis	Eyebright
Fagus sylvatica	Beech
Festuca ovina	Sheep's fescue (grass)
Festuca rubra	Red fescue (grass)
Fragaria vesca	Wild strawberry
Fraxinus excelsior	Ash
Galeobdolon luteum	Yellow archangel
Galium aparine	Goosegrass
Galium cruciata	Crosswort
Galium mollugo	Hedge bedstraw
Galium verum	Lady's bedstraw
Gentianella amarella	Felwort
Geranium robertianum	Herb robert
Geum urbanum	Wood avens
Glechoma hederacea	Ground ivy
Gymnadenia conopsea	Fragrant orchid
Hedera helix	Ivy
Helianthenum chamaecistus	Common rock rose
Heracleum sphondylium	Hogweed
Helictotrichon pratense	Meadow oat
Helictotrichon pubescens	Downy oat
Hieracium pilosella	Mouse-ear hawkweed
Hippocrepis comosa	Horseshoe vetch
Holcus lanatus	Yorkshire fog (grass)
Hypericum perforatum	Common St John's wort
Hypochoeris radicata	Common cat's-ear
Ilex aquifolium	Holly
Inula conyza	Ploughman's spikenard
Juniperus communis	Juniper
Knautia arvensis	Field scabious
Koeleria gracilis	Crested hair-grass
Lamium purpureum	Red dead-nettle
Leontodon autumnalis	Autumnal hawkbit
Leontodon hispidus	Greater hawkbit

Leontodon taraxacoides	Lesser hawkbit
Ligustrum vulgare	Privet
Linaria vulgaris	Common toadflax
Linum catharticum	Fairy flax
Listera ovata	Common twayblade
Lonicera periclymenum	Honeysuckle
Lotus corniculatus	Common bird's-foot trefoil
Luzula campestris	Field woodrush
Malus sylvestris	Crab-apple
Matricaria matricarioides	Pineapple mayweed
Medicago lupulina	Black medick
Melandrium album	White campion
Mercurialis perennis	Dog's mercury
Moehringia trinervia	Three-veined sandwort
Myosotis arvensis	Common forget-me-not
Myosotis discolor	Changing forget-me-not
Myosotis hispida	Early forget-me-not
Odontites verna	Red bartsia
Ononis repens	Restharrow
Ophrys apifera	Bee orchid
Ophrys muscifera (insectifera)	Fly orchid
Orchis fuchsii (dactylorhiza)	Spotted orchid
Orchis mascula	Early purple orchid
Orchis pyramidalis (anacamptis)	Pyramidal orchid
Origanum vulgare	Marjoram
Orobanche minor	Common broomrape
Pastinaca sativa	Wild parsnip
Phleum nodosum	Cat's-tail (grass)
Phleum pratense	Timothy (grass)
Phyteuma tenerum	Round-headed rampion
Plantago lanceolata	Ribwort plantain
Plantago major	Rat's-tail plantain
Plantago media	Hoary plantain
Plantanthera chlorantha	Greater butterfly orchid
Poa annua	Annual meadow grass
Polygala calcarea	Chalk milkwort
Polygala vulgaris	Common milkwort
Polygonum aviculare	Knotgrass
Potentilla anserina	Silverweed
Potentilla erecta	Tormentil
Potentilla reptans	Creeping cinquefoil
Potentilla sterilis	Barren strawberry
Poterium sanguisorba	Salad burnet

Primula veris	Cowslip
Prunella vulgaris	Self-heal
Prunus domesticus (institia)	Wild plum (bullace)
Prunus spinosa	Blackthorn (sloe)
Pulicaria dysenterica	Fleabane
Quercus cerris	Turkey oak
Quercus petiaea	Sessile oak
Quercus robur	Pedunculate oak
Ranunculus bulbosus	Bulbous buttercup
Ranunculus parviflorus	Small-flowered buttercup
Ranunculus repens	Creeping buttercup
Reseda lutea	Wild mignonette
Rhamnus cathartica	Common buckthorn
Rosa arvensis	Field rose
Rosa canina	Dog rose
Rosa rubiginosa	Sweetbriar
Rubus caesius	Dewberry
Rubus fruticosa	Bramble
Rumex acetosa	Common sorrel
Rumex crispus	Curled dock
Ruscus aculeatus	Butcher's broom
Salix caprea	Pussy willow
Sambucus nigra	Elder
Scabiosa columbaria	Small scabious
Sedum acre	Wall pepper (yellow stonecrop)
Senecio erucifolius	Hoary ragwort
Senecio jacobaea	Common ragwort
Senecio vulgaris	Groundsel
Silene vulgaris	Bladder campion
Sinapsis arvensis	Charlock
Solanum dulcamara	Bittersweet (woody nightshade)
Sonchus arvensis	Corn sow-thistle
Sonchus oleraceus	Smooth sow-thistle
Sorbus aria	Whitebeam
Spiranthes spirales	Autumn lady's tresses
Stachys sylvatica	Hedge woundwort
Stellaria graminea	Lesser stitchwort
Stellaria holostea	Greater stitchwort
Succisa pratensis	Small scabious
Tamus communis	Black bryony
Taraxacum officinale	Dandelion
Taxus baccata	Yew

Thelycrania sanguinea	Dogwood cornel
Thymns drucei	Wild thyme
Torilis japonica	Upright hedge parsley
Tragopogon pratensis	Goatsberd (Jack-go-to-bed-at-noon)
Trifolium dubium	Common yellow trefoil
Trifolium micranthum	Slender yellow trefoil
Trifolium pratense	Red clover
Trifolium repens	White clover
Trisetum flavescens	Yellow oat (grass)
Ulex europaeus	Gorse
Ulex minor	Lesser gorse
Urtica dioica	Stinging nettle
Valeriana officinalis	Common valerian
Verbascum thapsus	Common mullein
Verbena officinalis	Vervain
Veronica arvensis	Wall speedwell
Veronica chamaedrys	Bird's-eye speedwell
Veronica officinalis	Heath speedwell
Viburnum lantana	Wayfaring tree
Vicia angustifolia	Narrow-leaved vetch
Vicia cracca	Tufted vetch
Vicia sativa	Common vetch
Vicia sepium	Bush vetch
Viola hirta	Hairy violet
Viola riviana	Common dog violet
Zerna erecta	Upright brome (grass)

Results of orchid counts at Kingley Vale, various years 1964–77

Early purple orchid

Main valley

year	64	65	66	67	68	69	70	71	72	73	74	75
flowers	36	35	28	12	–*	9	3	2	0	0	0	0
leaves only	13	8	16	14	–	5	6	8	0	1	1	0

* No count

Western slope

In another glade on the western slope, an area of 50 square yards, numbers of early purple orchids have been counted throughout the years too, to measure their decline:

year	64	65	66	67	68	69	70	71	72	73	74	75	76	77
flowers	190	251	105	114	52	64	58	42	30	31	21	24	16	8
leaves only	209	109	182	135	117	97	105	71	59	72	34	31	28	21

Spotted orchid

Cp.	1964	1965	1967	1968	1969	1970	1975	1976	1977
5	25	20	19	17	37	52	26	81	16
6	8	17	41	38	51	58	107	4	21
8	0	0	0	0	3	1	0	0	0
9	0	0	0	0	0	1	0	0	0
13	4	0	11	5	4	8	22	11	4
15*	–	–	–	0	0	0	1	0	0
18	–	–	–	590	1445	1355	141	201	45

* The only compartment to have long grass; the others all have short turf

Fragrant orchid

Cp.	1964	1965	1967	1969	1970	1975	1976	1977
5	50	23	44	20	35	93	42	14

Bee orchid

Cp.	1964	1965	1967	1968	1969	1970	1975	1976	1977
5	26	26	34	21	37	22	33	10	17
6	40	97	40	8	5	5	21	4	15
8	0	0	14	0	0	0	0	0	0
9a	16	14	14	0	3	0	5	0	0
9b	0	0	5	0	0	0	63	0	7
11	7	6	4	6	1	0	4	0	5
13	84	80	114	89	87	65	64	52	59
17	0	1	0	1	0	0	0	0	.0
18	–	–	–	–	–	0	3	0	?

Pyramid orchid

Cp.	1964	1965	1967	1968	1969	1970	1975	1976	1977
5c	97	567	390	321	380	188	703	319	626
5a	62	82	87	50	46	20	23	55	125
9	118	193	120	43	0	28	129	51	5
13	0	0	1	1	0	0	0	0	0
18	–	–	–	–	–	–	123	46	31

Active management of the chalk grassland

Area 1   Plateau chalk grassland (Cps 11 and 12)

This area is primarily a chalk sward though with many patches of clay, giving local numbers of calcifuges such as tormentil, wood sage and heath violet among plants of the chalk such as salad burnet and milkwort. In 1964 this vegetation was roughly 3 feet high in June and was dominated by cocksfoot with emergent brambles. In 1970 it was cut for the first time as described, and litter removed. The first flowering season was remarkable for the numbers of common violets in the turf, followed by a white carpet of yarrow in August. By 1972 the grass was down to about 6 inches with many composites creeping in, autumn hawkbit making yellow carpets here and there but with a scattering of wild parsnip giving the area a rough appearance still. Even so, the cut was adjusted in June to knock out tall grasses like false oat and cocksfoot which were still seeding freely each year.

By 1974 the grass was down to a fairly short sward in August, with most flowers showing their flowering heads freely. Plants such as common hawkbit and harebell were beginning to flower again. It had been a difficult decision to cut the meadow in high summer because many hundreds of dark green fritillary butterflies were feeding on the purple and white flowers of the marsh thistles, and although they obviously were not going to be killed they would have to disperse – which they did, over a much wider area. Two seasons of summer cutting were enough to bring the rank grasses to heel. The cut is now taken after the flower-seed season has passed, in autumn.

The Thomas Transect   In 1954 a transect (a line plotted on a map and marked at hundred-foot intervals on the ground with posts) was laid out by Dr A. S. Thomas with the help of students from Reading University. The first part of this transect runs through the plateau, continuing on down to the very southern end some 4000 feet away. It was recorded by a 10-pin frame being placed at right angles to the transect line every 20 feet, the pins being 2 inches apart. Whatever touched any one or more of the pins was recorded. Thomas touched 26 species of plants between the 1st and 3rd posts. Today (1977) there are 12 species at these points, the most abundant being bramble which was not touched once in 1954, but which now completely dominates 90 per cent of this line. Neither this transect line nor the vegetation 5 yards on either side has ever been cut, in order to keep a permanent record of vegetation changes post-myxomatosis.

The fortunes of this piece of hillside are summarised below from the recordings made in spring each year (thus some summer-flowering species were not included), six species being picked out to represent the changing state of the grassland:

	1954	1957	1961	1977
Average height	4.1 in	6.4 in	4.9 in	5 ft
	(10.5 cm)	(16.5 cm)	(12.5 cm)	(1.5 m)
No. of species touched	21	20	28	12
Sweet vernal grass	4	15	35	2
Sheep's fescue grass	89	85	76	11
Crested hair-grass	49	36	40	4
Carnation and glaucous sedge	22	20	14	3
Salad burnet	34	36	40	7
Bramble	0	1	10	61

Area 2 Valley grassland (Cp. 3)

Dr Thomas recorded the eastern side of this area on the transect between the 28th and 30th posts. In 1954 he touched 27 species. Today on this untouched transect there are 16 species and the whole area is dominated by tufts of false oat grass.

	1954	1957	1961	1977
				1 ft 6 in–
Average height	3.7 in	7 in	6.1 in	6 ft 6 in
	(9.5 cm)	(18 cm)	(15.5 cm)	(40–200)
No. of species touched	27	24	18	16
Sweet vernal grass	9	20	13	0
Cocksfoot grass	2	10	28	5
Sheep's fescue grass	71	89	74	0
Yorkshire fog grass	1	17	32	0
Crested hair-grass	36	32	28	0
Salad burnet	26	34	29	0

It now resembles not so much grassland as emergent woodland. Plants lost completely on these points since 1954 are golden oat, sheep's fescue, crested dog's-tail, cat's-tail, sweet vernal, crested hair, bird's-eye speedwell, common dog violet, ribwort, plantain, salad burnet, common hawkbit, ox-eye daisy, cushion calamint, field woodrush, mouse-ear hawkweed, eyebright, wild parsnip and stemless thistle. Plants gained are bramble, honeysuckle, traveller's joy, hawthorn, dogwood and lesser stitchwort. The highest valence is for false oat with 43, and bramble comes closest second with 38.

It is interesting to see how woodland evolves out of such a tall suffocating sward of false oat or upright brome, as is being demonstrated here. Tiny seedlings like yew, oak and hawthorn cannot regenerate or survive in this yard-high sward. Instead they wait until bramble, with its long arching runners, spreads like an octopus and then they grow up from underneath.

In order to try and reclaim the chalk turf, an area west of the transect was mown, starting in 1968. When cutting began, a yearly check was made on this grassland, recording all the species present in late July when the flower season is at its peak and just before it is cut (though in the first two seasons it was cut in June to knock out the tall grass). The total area is divided into two: in one half the grass litter is collected and removed, while in the other it is left lying on the surface. Time will show if these treatments produce varying results in the species present. The recording is made by random throws of a yard-square wire frame. The recorder walks the area throwing the frame down about every ten paces, and then recording all the plants found within the frame. The Domin Scale of Abundance is used. This scale gives a number according to the percentage cover of each plant within the square yard, and is as follows:

10 = 100%	6 = 25–33%	2 = cover scarce c. 3%
9 = 75%	5 = 20%	1 = cover very scarce c. 2%
8 = 50–75%	4 = 5%	x = isolated
7 = 33–50%	3 = small c. 4%	

Ten squares are recorded in each side of the total cut area, making twenty in all. On the table below, the average figure from the ten squares is given to show the total picture for each year. This work has to be done very slowly and carefully. It takes time to 'get the eye in', not just to identify the plants but to decide how many of any one species there are within the square.

The effects of mowing on chalk grassland

	Cut but not collected							Cut and collected						
	70	71	72	73	74	75	77	70	71	72	73	74	75	77
Achillea millefolium (Yarrow)	3	2	3	4	3	2	4	2	3	2	2	3	3	3
Agrimonia eupatoria (Agrimony)		x	x	x			–			x			x	
Agrostis stolonifera (White bent grass)	2	2	1	1	4	2	4	1	3	1	2	3	3	4
Anthoxanthum odoratum (Sweet vernal grass)	x	x	1	4	2	4	1		1	1	4	1	4	1
Arenaria leptoclados (Small thyme-leaved sandwort)		x	2		1	x	1					1	x	1
Arrhenatherum elatius (False oat grass)		x	3	x			–		x	3			x	x
Bare ground			1	x	2	1	1			x	1	3	x	2
Briza media (Quaking grass)			x			1	x		x				1	1
Campanula glomerata (Clustered bellflower)										x				
Campanula rotundifolia (Harebell)	x		x			x	x	1	1	x		1	x	1
Carex caryophyllea (Spring sedge)						x								x
Carex flacca (Glaucous sedge)	x			x	1	2	x	x		x	x	1	1	1
Cerastium sp. (Chickweed sp.)					x	x	1					x	1	x

	Cut but not collected							Cut and collected						
	70	71	72	73	74	75	77	70	71	72	73	74	75	77
Cirsium acaulon (Dwarf thistle)		x	x	x	x	x							x	x
Cirsium arvense (Creeping thistle)		x	x	x	x						x	x	x	
Cirsium palustre (Marsh thistle)					x	x	x		x	x				x
Clinopodium vulgare (Wild basil)	2	3	4	4	4	3		3	3	3	2	3	3	3
Crataegus mon (Hawthorn)				x							x			
Dactylis glomerata (Cocksfoot)	2	2	1	2	1	x	1	2	2	2	x	x	x	1
Euonymus europaeus (Spindle)		x		x		x			x	x	x			
Euphrasia officinalis (Eyebright)	x	x	x				x						x	1
Festuca rubra (Red fescue)	5	5	6	5	6	5	5	4	4	5	5	5	4	5
Fragaria vesca (Wild strawberry)					x				x					
Galium verum (Lady's bedstraw)	4	4	3	4	4	4	4	4	4	3	4	4	4	4
Glechoma hederacea (Ground ivy)	x	x	x	1	1	x		x	x		x			
Heligtotrichon pratense (Meadow oat)	3	5	4	5	4	3	3	7	6	5	6	5	4	4
Hieracium pilosella (Mouse-ear hawkweed)					x	x							x	1
Holcus lanatus (Yorkshire fog)	3	5	4	4	4	5	2	4	4	4	3	3	5	2
Hypericum perforatum (Common St John's wort)											x			x
Koelaria gracilis (Crested hair-grass)			x		x	1	1				x	1		x
Knautia arvensis (Field scabious)					x								x	
Leontodon autumnalis (Autumn hawkbit)			x	x	1	2	2	x		x	x	1	2	2
Leontodon hispidus (Greater hawkbit)	1	1	1	1	1	2	2	1	2	2	2	2	2	2
Linum catharticum (Fairy flax)	x				x	x	x							
Lonicera (Honeysuckle)			x	x	x		x	x	x	x		x	x	◀x
Lotus corniculatus (Common bird's-foot trefoil)	1	1	1	1	1	2	2	x	1	1	1	1	1	2
Luzula campestris (Field woodrush)						x								x
Medicago lupulina (Black medick)			x		x		x							

	Cut but not collected							Cut and collected						
	70	71	72	73	74	75	77	70	71	72	73	74	75	77
Myosotis sp. (Forget-me-not)					x	x					x			x
Pastinica sativa (Wild parsnip)	3	2	1	2	2	2	2	3	2	1	2	1	2	2
Phleum nodosum (Cat's-tail grass)	1	x	x	2	1	x	2		2	x	1		1	1
Plantago lanceolata (Ribwort plantain)	2	2	2	2	4	4	4	1	3	2	3	4	4	4
Potentilla erecta (Tormentil)				x										
Poterium sanquisorba (Salad burnet)	4	3	2	2	2	3	3	2	4	2	2	3	3	3
Prunella vulgaris (Self-heal)			x		x		x				x	x	x	
Prunus spinosa (Blackthorn)					x						x			
Quercus (Oak)									x	x			x	
Ranunculus sp. (Buttercup sp.)					x									
Rumex acetosa (Common sorrel)	2	2	1	1	2	1	2	1	x	x	x	1	1	2
Scabiosa columbaria (Small scabious)						1					x			x
Senecio jacobea (Common ragwort)			x	x		x	x			x			x	x
Sonchus arvensis (Corn sow-thistle)	x	1	x	x	x	x	x	1	1	1	x	1	x	x
Taraxacum officinalis (Dandelion)	x		x	x	x	x	x		x	x	x		x	
Thymus drucei (Wild thyme)	x		x		x	x					x			
Trifolium pratense (Red clover)			x		x		x				x			x
Trisetum flavescens (Yellow oat)				1			2				1	x		1
Veronica chamaedrys (Bird's-eye speedwell)	x		x	x	1	1	1	x		x	x	1	1	1
Viola hirta (Hairy violet)	x	x	x	x	1	1	x	1	1	x	x	1	1	1
Viola riviniana (Common dog violet)					x		x				x	x		
Zerna erecta (Upright brome)	1	1	2		1	1	2	1	x		2	2	1	1
Total no. of species	26	26	36	37	43	38	43	23	26	34	33	39	35	45

Note: No count was made in 1976 due to the drought.

The number of species has steadily increased, the notable newcomers after three years of cutting being attractive flowers such as mouse-ear hawkweed, dog violet, agrimony and self-heal. Others like bird's-foot trefoil, salad burnet, bird's-eye speedwell, glaucous sedge, lady's bedstraw, Yorkshire fog grass and crested hair-grass more or less held their own and then began to increase. Field scabious and tormentil appeared briefly after four years of cutting and are probably beginning to consolidate their root hold. Rather coarse and 'weedy' species that have but a small place in a genuine chalk turf were prominent in the early years and then began to decline. These included wild parsnip, cocksfoot grass, ground ivy and corn sow-thistle.

Clearly we are aiming in the right direction, but there may be unforeseen setbacks which will divert the grassland temporarily from its smooth progression towards becoming a well-integrated community.

Area 3   Western slope (Cp. 5)

No systematic recording has been carried out over this one-acre plot that runs alongside the outer track ascending the hill. But a glance at its summer flowers in comparison to the rough sward of upright brome to the east shows how it is responding to treatment. The grass is collected. After five years it was unnecessary to cut the turf either that year (1975) or the next, except for the southern end where cocksfoot grass has not yet been eliminated. Ribwort plantain, salad burnet and hawkbit predominate in the northern half together with some milkwort, thyme, rock rose and fairy flax. But the success of this meadow is partly due to some rabbit grazing that has been concentrated into this 'glade' among the rougher, less palatable swards of upright brome nearby. It is also helped by the grazing of deer.

Area 4   Orchid sites (Cps 5 and 13)

Sundry small banks and tracksides are mown by lawnmower in order to prevent upright brome from forming dense, suffocating tufts over orchid sites. These amount to no more than half an acre in all.

Area 5   The paddock (Cp. 9a)

Buttons and George were two grey gelding New Forest ponies bought for £80 apiece by John Maylam, the warden of a Kentish reserve, in 1971 at a New Forest sale. Neither had been broken in. They arrived one foggy November afternoon for their task of clearing 17 acres of derelict chalk grassland in the steep gully and valley floor, an area that had last seen a domesticated grazing animal in 1938. Six hundred seedling yews had been cleared from this paddock, a somewhat unusual operation on a yew forest nature reserve, but one that was necessary if grassland was to maintained. Several were not discovered until a year after the ponies had been browsing upon them, with no ill effects.

Three more ponies came to the reserve within a year, and by April 1975 they had completed their task and were moved on to Lullington Heath, where today they are eating their way through 70 acres of gorse. Between them they removed the inhibiting blanket of old brome grass which for so long had smothered the turf, and within two years pyramid orchids were blooming in dozens on the valley slopes. Bee orchids as well had an open grassland once again, and 30 flowers were counted for the first time in this gulley. Milkwort and hairy violet returned, having been all but choked out of existence. False oat grass on the valley floor gave way to sheep's fescue grass, but for a time ragwort and wild parsnip proliferated. This was because the ponies were too heavy on their feet and gashed open the turf, especially during the wet winter of 1974–5. However, this upsurge of ragwort was probably inevitable with the opening up of the ground after so long a time.

Forty-eight sheep (Dorset Horn × Scot's Halfbred ewe lambs) were brought into this paddock in April 1977 to continue the grazing. After the 1976 drought very little tall vegetation other than shrubby plants existed at all at this date. But as soon as the grass began to grow, the sheep could only just keep pace with the upsurge of upright brome and false oat that would otherwise have blanketed the slopes once again, as they had before the advent of the ponies. At first the sheep were more used to an 'egg and chips' diet of perennial rye grass, and would not eat a number of more unusual herbs. These included strawberry, marjoram, wood sage, spring forget-me-not and biting stonecrop. Neither would they eat unpalatable grass such as upright brome and tor. Even the agricultural crop grass, cocksfoot, was ignored if it grew more than six inches high in a small tuft. They obviously enjoyed sheep's fescue, salad burnet, ragwort, hoary and ribwort plantains, hairy violet and small-flowered buttercup. It was not long before they got a taste for Yorkshire fog grass and then the tufts of cocksfoot were taken, while the common hawkbit, bird's-eye speedwell, dandelion, thyme and even the strong-smelling and blister-forming (on horses' lips as well as human skin) wild parsnip came into their diet before two weeks had passed. I was particularly glad to see this rank weed disappear, for I had spent some time each year cutting it back.

When the grass failed to grow quickly in spring 1977 due to inhibiting north-east winds, the sheep soon found that they had to tackle plants hitherto ignored. By early June they were grazing biting stonecrop and spring speedwell, until these very plentiful early colonisers from the drought of 1976 began to take their place in the multitudinous mosaic. The tufts of brome were grazed down in this hungry period too. But some plants have never been touched: weld, ploughman's spikenard, all thistles (except sometimes stemless), nettle, wood sage, yellow mullein.

The sheep at first showed little comprehension of woody species. They treated the brambles like a keen but novice athlete would a set of hurdles, and about three had to be extricated every day. By early June they had discovered that brambles were for eating, not jumping, and a browse-line quickly developed, even more deeply indented than that made by deer. They even learned how to get inside the bushes to graze straggling grasses, without getting hooked up. So far the sheep have proved to be excellent graziers, except for one thing: their habit of digging out little platforms on the steep slope in which to rest (as I had seen Marco Polo sheep doing in the mountains of the Hindu Kush) has created small bare places. Otherwise, they are light on their feet and have not cut open the turf as the ponies had done. There have been no problems with dogs, as the sheep so far are not frightened of them; I take mine into the paddock frequently and they walk boldly up to her, stamping their feet. I think timid sheep are often the cause of sheep worrying. However, I check the fencing frequently to make sure that dogs stay out and the sheep stay in.

Area 6 The south-east spur (Cp. 13)

On the south-east spur there was a very rough area which was rapidly degenerating. Because of its uneven nature it would have been almost impossible to cut it by mechanical means. A local man had enquired whether we had any grazing for his three donkeys. So I set about enclosing a three-acre paddock with a fence, which was not quite such a daunting task as enclosing the main paddock.

The paddock had two things I particularly wanted to conserve. One was a splendid group of several dozen buckthorn bushes on which a large colony of brimstone butterflies always thrive. Their emergence and exodus in a yellow swarm over the spur and down into the main valley in the late summer is one of the great sights of this reserve. The other was the clump of round-headed rampion which is described on pp. 95–6. I was pretty sure that the donkeys would not eat the buckthorn, but they would eat the tall grass, thus probably killing off the rampion and all the other chalk flora.

The lease was signed and the three animals arrived in mid-April 1976. The ensuing drought did not seem to bother them despite the grass turning brown, for they ate hawthorn which supplied a fair amount of moisture. In the following cold and miserably wet winter they turned their backs on the wind and finished off all the privet and half the hawthorn – that is, they reduced the bushes to half their size by breaking off and eating all twigs and small branches. How they could take so many spines into their mouths without harm I do not know. They were very careful as they did so, looking like elderly people biting pieces of rock with false teeth. Not one buckthorn bush was touched, neither were the one or two yew trees. Wayfaring, blackthorn, bramble, dogwood, and one juniper bush were all destroyed.

Before the donkeys arrived I recorded ten one-yard-square plots in different parts of the paddock, and two years later I recorded the same plots again. The following table shows the results. Figures refer to the Domin Scale (see p. 181).

Species	18 July 1975										7 July 1977									
	Plots: 1	2	3	4	5	6	7	8	9	10	1	2	3	4	5	6	7	8	9	10
White bent grass			x			4										x	2		1	2
Upright brome					9	8	9	9	7							8	8	7	7	7
Soft brome grass	4	1									8	4	4	5	4					
Sweet vernal grass			5	4	5						1		2							

186

	18 July 1975										7 July 1977									
Species Plots:	1	2	3	4	5	6	7	8	9	10	1	2	3	4	5	6	7	8	9	10
Downy oat grass	4	5	5	8	7	3	1	1	4	2	4	5	2	4	6	1	2	4	5	
Yorkshire fog grass	7	6	6	5	5						4	5	6	5	4					
Sheep's fescue grass	6	7	8	5	5	5	7	4	2	7	4	5	5	4	5	5	4	5	6	5
Cocksfoot grass					x									1						
Common meadow grass								x												x
Smaller cat's-tail											x								x	x
Yarrow	1	3	2	3	3	2	x	x	x	3	1	4	4	4	5	2		x	1	1
Sheep sorrel	3	3	3	3	3						2	4	2	4	4					
Ribwort plantain	1				x	1	2		3		1	1			1	1	1	1	1	
Common hawkbit					x											x				
Autumn hawkbit												1								
Salad burnet					x	3											x	4	x	x
Wild parsnip					x		2	3	2								x	x		x 1
Lady's bedstraw					x															
Bird's-foot trefoil							x	3												x
Dandelion						x											x	1		
Musk thistle											1	1	1	x		x		1	1	
Thyme-leaved sandwort													x		4					
Small thyme-leaved sandwort											2	2	2	4	2	x				
Ragwort											1	x								
Soft milk thistle													x	x		1	1		1	1
Chickweed																	1			
Spring forget-me-not																	1			
Field poppy																				x
Bare ground											5	4	4	5	4	4	5	4	4	7
No. of species										18										28

The changes have not necessarily been for the better despite the increase in species, since many of the newcomers are 'weed' species such as ragwort and poppy. This is predictable because the meadow is bounded on two sides by farmland. The 1976 drought opened up large patches of bare ground as well and these remained into 1977. But there have been some changes for the better, notably an increase in sheep's fescue and a decrease in upright brome. Elsewhere in the meadow there is a noticeable improvement visually in the sward, with some really good areas of chalk turf. Thyme has increased in many places, and so has salad burnet and lady's bedstraw. The recorded areas which are those most in need of improvement may take many years of grazing before they begin to look anything like a chalk turf.

Thin soils (Cp. 8)

Some grasslands have been maintained in a perfect short-sward state by thin, dry soils and a small amount of rabbit grazing. One such area is on the low ridge that bisects the twin gullies of the valley. Although it has no orchids, it is probably the finest piece of turf on the reserve and occupies several acres,

187

running in glades among the isolated old yew trees. The transect crosses this area and so we are able to see how it has, remarkably, changed very little since 1954, despite the fact that a much-used track runs within a few yards of the transect line. This track is unbroken turf but it is so completely different in species composition – being dominated largely by daisies – that one is thankful that people walk in straight lines between points A and B. The only management that occurs over this grassland is the removal of scrub and ragwort.

Species	No. of touches per 50 pins	
	30 March 1954	9 April 1977
Sheep's fescue grass	45	39
White bent grass	4	0
Downy oat grass	18	18
Crested dog's-tail grass	3	0
Crested hair-grass	0	1
Field woodrush	0	1
Upright brome grass	0	10
Common cat's-tail grass	6	0
Glaucous sedge	5	3
Thyme	15	21
Squinancywort	10	3
Salad burnet	15	13
Mouse-ear hawkweed	4	6
Stemless thistle	1	0
Harebell	1	4
Ribwort plantain	1	11
Self-heal	2	0
Heath bedstraw	1	9
Lady's bedstraw	0	1
Dandelion	1	2
Common hawkbit	0	1
Moss (*Pseudoscleropodium purum*)	15	12
Lichen (*Cladonia*)	1	0
No. of species	18	17
Average height of vegetation	4in (10cm)	1½in (4cm)
Rabbit pellets per frame	11	7

The obvious changes to be seen are the spread of upright brome and the increase of plantain, probably due to increased human trampling. But the increase in thyme and decrease in squinancywort is unexplained. Of course there are many more species in this grassland than are touched, but only a representative sample of plants will ever be recorded on a line transect which merely records the rate of change.

Now compare this with a similar grassland a little lower down the slope which has always been crossed by a bridlepath. This is the main gulley route which is probably crossed by 5000 people a year (2000 p.a. in 1954). It was recorded at the same time of year, early April.

Once more upright brome has invaded, this time with bramble and false oat

Species	No. of touches per 50 pins	
	1954	*1977*
Sheep's fescue grass	15	13
White bent grass	20	0
Meadow oat grass	1	0
Downy oat grass	4	0
Crested dog's-tail grass	3	0
Crested hair-grass	0	1
Upright brome grass	0	25
False oat grass	0	8
Rough meadow grass	1	0
Yorkshire fog grass	13	0
Glaucous sedge	2	4
Thyme	2	1
Salad burnet	5	3
Mouse-ear hawkweed	1	3
Harebell	1	0
Ribwort plantain	2	10
Self-heal	3	2
Hoary plantain	0	1
Hedge bedstraw	0	1
Common hawkbit	0	5
Autumn hawkbit	4	1
Strawberry clover	2	1
Bird's-foot trefoil	4	0
Bulbous buttercup	4	0
Ragwort	1	0
Daisy	0	4
Yarrow	0	9
Bramble	0	21
Traveller's joy	0	3
Moss (*Pseudoscleropodium purum*)	1	0
Moss (sp. unknown)	1	6
Bare ground	0	1
No. of species	21	20
Average height of vegetation	$\frac{1}{2}$–6in (1–15cm)	$\frac{1}{2}$–18in (1–46cm)
Rabbit pellets per frame	5	8

grass because the ground is damper and richer. No doubt twenty years of picnic debris and trampling have helped to enrich the ground here. What is surprising perhaps is how the very common Yorkshire fog grass dies out so quickly even though it is somewhat coarse and always invades any waste land. However I have noticed the same behaviour on any area that I clear. For the first year Yorkshire fog fills in former bramble-covered ground very quickly, but within three of four years it has gone. But delicate and elusive plants like harebell do not like trampling at all. The lack of ragwort probably reflects the all-out war waged upon it for thirteen years. The increase in plantain warns us that in the section between the 14th and 15th posts we could be approaching a similar state of affairs with the horrors of daisies in turf if people persist in widening the path at that higher area of grassland.

Analysis of the Common Bird Census
at Kingley Vale
(under the aegis of the British Trust for Ornithology)

During the ten-year period covered by the Common Bird Census, 57 species have held territories in the study area and 46 of these (83 per cent) have bred in a majority of the years. These qualify for a count of '1' in Table I (pp. 193–4), in which all the species are shown. Numerical details of the bird community are provided in Table II, showing the percentages of passerines or passeriformes.

Passerines are the perching songbirds and form the largest order of the bird world. They include the lark family, swallows, pipits and wagtails, shrikes, orioles, starlings, waxwings, the crow family, dippers, wrens, accentors, warblers, flycatchers, the thrush family, the tit family, treecreepers, finches and buntings.

As can be seen from Table III, chaffinch and robin are the dominant species, together forming over one-fifth of the breeding bird community at Kingley Vale. Wood pigeon, blackbird, wren and dunnock are subdominant, and the six species together make up one half of the total breeding pairs found on the reserve.

The yew–oak mixture and its associated variety of scrub growth in the valley bottom has the richest diversity of bird species (Table IV). In addition to the 30 passerine species enumerated in Table II, there are pheasant, woodpigeon, turtle dove and woodcock. Higher up the valley where the scrub is composed mainly of brambles, partridges of both species are present, and the skylark sometimes encroaches from the plateau. This is the best area for the whitethroat and yellowhammer, with the grasshopper warbler regularly appearing until 1975. Meadow and tree pipit territories sometimes overlap at the head of the valley. Green woodpeckers feed regularly at the ant-hills of the yellow ant (*Lasius flavus*) and kestrels and sparrowhawks hunt over the valley floor. Altogether some 34 species (85 per cent of these recorded in the study area) are associated with the yew–oak scrub.

Of the passerine species only nine, plus the pheasant and woodpigeon, enter the young yew wood, and five of these are absent from it in some years. It is possibly a marginal habitat, acceptable only in years of high population for the wren, dunnock, great tit and song thrush. At best it attracts only one-fifth of the species regularly inhabiting the reserve. Chaffinch, robin and blackbird are the only birds which have held territory in all years, and which usually have more than one pair present. This great loss of species diversity reflects the sterility of the 'monospecies' yew woodland once the canopy has closed and suppressed the scrub.

The situation is better in the middle-aged wood, with 15 passerine species present regularly, two others occasionally, and in addition pheasant, wood-pigeon, tawny owl and green woodpecker. Thus over one-third of the total species occur here. This is a marginal habitat for blackcap and chiffchaff: these

190

two 'high forest' warblers, prominent in the yew–oak scrub with its scattered tall trees, avoid the closed canopy of the young yew completely and enter the present stage only as 'edge' species, where they have ready access to the islands of yew families and scrub. Wren and dunnock also show a marked tendency to occupy the wood edge.

The mixture of a broad-leaved canopy and the greater availability of nest-sites in holes in the mature yew–ash wood induces colonisation by a larger variety of species – about 70 per cent of the total recorded on the census study area. Golden pheasant, stockdove, jackdaw, nuthatch and starling confine their nesting activities to this zone. It is perhaps surprising that neither blue tits nor marsh tits are regular occupants of this habitat, since suitable nesting-holes are readily available.

Non-passerines
A pair of shelduck has frequently been observed in the grassland in the centre of the census study area, exhibiting nesting tendencies such as the inspection of rabbit burrows, but they have not bred so far.

Kestrels nested at the edge of the mature yew–ash wood in 1971–6; they have been present on the reserve during most years, and the sparrowhawk is almost as regular. English partridges are well dispersed about the open areas, and their 1971 total of six pairs is an improvement on their previous best figures, five and four respectively in 1964–5, but they have declined since 1973. Pheasants are widely scattered in all the habitat types, and their numbers have shown little change despite the rearing and release of about 8000 birds annually near the area between 1965–74. The golden pheasant, present annually since 1968, has a marked preference for the yew–ash wood.

Woodpigeons are only estimated and the population probably averages about 30 pairs in all habitat types. Stockdoves (perhaps two pairs each year) occupy the yew–ash wood. Earlier censuses of the reserve record two pairs of tawny owls in the older yew woods in 1964 and 1965; these have now increased to three. Pairs of barn owls hunted over the reserve regularly in the early years, and have sometimes bred in recent years.

There was a pair of great spotted woodpeckers in each of the years 1964–7 inclusive, and they have usually been found since then. A lesser spotted woodpecker was seen once in 1977. The environment is obviously much better suited to the green woodpecker and in some years before and during the census work four or five pairs have been present. Five were present in 1973, but only two in 1976 and three in 1977.

Passerines
Crow family (*Corvidae*)   The pair of jackdaws did not appear on the census plot until 1967, although there are records of a colony in the mature yew–ash wood twenty-five years ago. There were two pairs of magpies in 1964 and one in 1965, with some probably breeding in 1970. Since gamekeeping to the south of the reserve ceased in 1974 they have increased. The two pairs of jays may have

been exceeded in 1964–5: sightings of this species are well dispersed over all habitat types.

Tit family (*Paridae*)   Tits make up 10 per cent of the bird community, and coal tit and great tit appear in all habitats; either one may be dominant. The great tit is usually twice as common as the blue tit, a reversal of the situation found in most kinds of broad-leaved woodland in England. At Kingley Vale the marsh tit is one-third as common as the blue tit and both largely inhabit the yew–oak scrub.

Nuthatch probably nested from 1963 to 1965 inclusive in the yew–ash wood.
The treecreeper family (*Certhidae*) may have bred at the same period but is now rarely seen.

Wren family (*Troglodytidae*)   Few of the wren territories are actually contained within the yew, it being much more an 'edge' species than the other common inhabitants, chaffinch, robin and blackbird. Only very occasionally is a territory established in the young yew wood. Only a single wren territory was recorded in 1963, the first breeding season after the disastrously severe winter of 1962–3 when the national level of the wren population fell by 79 per cent, as determined by the Common Bird Census (Williamson and Homes, 1964). The species increased to six pairs by 1964, 10 in 1965, and 11 in 1966, almost doubling to 21 pairs in 1967. It rose to 30 in 1974. The habitats preferred during recolonisation were firstly the yew–oak scrub, followed by the edge of the yew–ash wood and latterly the middle-aged yew where this opens on to scrub.

Thrush family (*Turdinae*)   The distribution of song records for the song thrush in 1970 showed an apparent liking for the mature yew–ash, but in later years there was a predominance in the middle-aged yew and scrub. This has now returned to the yew–oak. They are not usually found in the young yew wood. On a national scale, as measured by the Common Bird Census results, song thrushes were reduced by 59 per cent following the severe 1962–3 winter (Williamson and Homes, 1964). Only four pairs were found in the reserve but recovery was good and the species was back to ten pairs in 1964. Similarly blackbird numbers were low in 1963 (14 pairs) but they were above average in 1964.

The nightingales invariably choose a specialised habitat of close-growing scrub up to 15 feet in height associated with clumps of mature oaks and adjacent young yews growing on the valley floor.

Warbler family (*Sylviinae*)   One, sometimes two, pairs of grasshopper warblers were present from 1963 to 1966; they have not been recorded in recent years.

Both blackcaps and chiffchaffs prefer 'edge' territories where the yew and the yew–ash woodland meet open ground. In one year a pair of garden warblers did likewise, but usually a single pair inhabits the yew–oak scrub. Willow warblers and both species of whitethroats also choose the yew–oak scrub and an occasional sedge warbler has appeared in this habitat – probably a late passage migrant.

Other passerines The goldcrest (family *Regulidae*) is fairly evenly spread throughout the mature and middle-aged woods but avoids the young yew stand in the north-east. The yew–oak scrub appears to suit it well. There were two pairs only after the severe winter of 1962–3, but they had increased to 13 by 1965. The spotted flycatcher (family *Muscicapidae*) is occasionally recorded.

Practically all the dunnocks are in 'edge' territories either among the yew–oak (the most favoured habitat) or where the older yew woods encroach on the scrub. They have, with robins, recently invaded pure bramble areas. Of the finch family (*Fringillidae*), two pairs of hawfinches and one or two pairs of goldfinches were present in 1964–5. An occasional corn bunting (family *Emberizidae*) sings on the boundary of the reserve, coinciding with cereal crops.

Table I   Birds breeding at Kingley Vale, 1967–77

	67	68	69	70	71	72	73	74	75	76	77
Sparrowhawk (*Accipiter nisis*)	–	–	1	*	*	–	1	1	1	–	*
Kestrel (*Falco tinnunculus*)	1	*	1	1	1	1	1	1	1	1	1
Red-legged partridge (*Alectoris barbara*)	–	–	–	*	*	*	1	*	1	1	1
Grey partridge (*Perdix perdix*)	1	2	2	3	6	3	3	*	–	*	*
Pheasant (*Phasianus colchicus*)	15	13	12	15	17	16	16	16	14	13	14
Golden pheasant (*Chrysolophus pictus*)	–	–	1	–	*	–	*	–	1	1	*
Lapwing (*Vanellus vanellus*)	–	–	–	–	2	1	1	1	1	1	–
Woodcock (*Scolopax rusticola*)	–	–	1	*	1	2	2	2	2	1	1
Woodpigeon (*Columba palumbus*) (estimated)	30	30	30	30	30	30	30	30	30	30	30
Stockdove (*Columba oenas*)	–	–	*	1	*	1	*	*	1	1	3
† Turtle dove (*Streptopelia turtur*)	1	2	3	2	3	1	2	2	1	1	2
† Cuckoo (*Cuculua canorus*)	1	2	1	2	1	8	1	2	1	1	1
Barn owl (*Tyto alba*)	–	–	*	–	1	–	1	*	*	–	–
Little owl (*Athene noctua*)	–	–	–	–	–	–	?1	*	–	*	–
Tawny owl (*Strix aluco*)	*	1	–	1	1	2	1	2	2	3	1
Long-eared owl (*Asio otus*)	–	–	–	–	–	1	*	–	–	–	–
† Nightjar (*Caprimulgus europaeus*)	–	–	–	–	–	*	1	1	–	1	–
Green woodpecker (*Picus viridis*)	2	1	3	4	4	2	5	4	3	2	3
Great spotted woodpecker (*Dendrocopas major*)	1	1	*	–	*	–	1	1	*	*	*
Skylark (*Alauda arvensis*)	1	1	1	1	1	*	*	*	2	*	2
Tree pipit (*Anthus trivialis*)	1	–	1	–	1	*	2	2	1	–	*
Meadow pipit (*Anthus pratensis*)	1	*	–	1	2	*	*	1	*	–	*
Jay (*Garrulus glandarius*)	1	1	2	2	1	2	2	1	1	2	1
Magpie (*Pica pica*)	–	–	–	*	–	–	–	1	2	2	2
Jackdaw (*Corvus monedula*)	1	1	1	1	*	1	1	*	1	1	1
Carrion crow (*Corvus corone corone*)	2	2	2	2	*	1	1	1	1	1	1
Wren (*Troglodytes troglodytes*)	21	19	18	16	18	23	22	30	26	18	13
Dunnock (*Prunella modularis*)	15	15	16	19	19	18	13	14	15	15	11
† Grasshopper warbler (*Locustella naevia*)	*	*	–	*	*	1	*	*	*	–	–
† Garden warbler (*Sylvia borin*)	1	1	1	1	1	–	*	*	1	1	*
† Blackcap (*Sylvia atricapilla*)	9	8	8	6	5	6	*	4	4	8	4
† Whitethroat (*Sylvia communis*)	19	23	11	7	10	7	4	2	3	11	12
† Lesser whitethroat (*Sylvia curruca*)	2	3	3	2	2	1	1	*	1	3	2
† Willow warbler (*Phylloscopus trochilus*)	8	7	7	15	10	13	16	15	5	14	8
† Chiffchaff (*Phylloscopus collybita*)	9	8	8	8	7	7	8	5	3	2	2
Goldcrest (*Regulus regulus*)	6	9	11	11	13	8	6	7	5	3	3
† Spotted flycatcher (*Muscicapa striata*)	*	*	*	–	1	–	*	–	–	–	–
Robin (*Erithacus rubecula*)	38	38	37	28	27	27	27	32	21	38	49
† Nightingale (*Luscinia megarhynchos*)	5	8	5	4	2	1	3	2	2	3	2

	67	68	69	70	71	72	73	74	75	76	77
Blackbird (*Turdus merula*)	30	25	31	24	20	28	23	17	18	19	19
Song thrush (*Turdus philomelos*)	12	5	6	4	7	4	5	5	2	2	3
Mistle thrush (*Turdus viscivorus*)	1	2	1	3	2	4	3	2	3	3	4
Marsh tit (*Parus palustris*)	4	4	2	3	1	1	1	1	2	4	2
Blue tit (*Parus caeruleus*)	4	5	2	4	7	16	7	5	5	6	6
Coal tit (*Parus ater*)	20	13	10	10	12	17	16	12	5	11	11
Great tit (*Parus major*)	12	13	10	11	16	16	12	9	9	10	13
Long-tailed tit (*Aegithalos caudatus*)	1	*	1	1	1	2	1	2	3	3	3
Nuthatch (*Sitta europaea*)	1	1	–	–	1	1	1	*	–	1	–
Treecreeper (*Certhia familiaris*)	–	–	–	*	1	–	*	–	–	–	–
Chaffinch (*Fringilla coelebs*)	39	41	33	29	36	37	33	33	31	31	21
Bullfinch (*Pyrrhula pyrrhula*)	10	5	6	8	10	10	6	5	8	4	5
Greenfinch (*Carduelis chloris*)	1	1	9	1	3	7	8	1	1	1	3
Goldfinch (*Carduelis carduelis*)	1	1	1	–	–	1	–	–	–	*	–
Linnet (*Acanthis cannabina*)	8	6	3	4	1	–	–	1	?	–	1
Corn bunting (*Emberiza calandra*)	–	–	–	–	–	–	–	–	–	*	*
† Yellowhammer (*Emberiza citrinella*)	14	6	9	14	11	8	11	5	6	5	7
Starling (*Sturnus vulgaris*)	–	*	1	1	*	1	5	1	2	1	2

Total: 57 species
No. of pairs   350 324 311 300 318 336 306 279 246 280 270

* Bird present but breeding not verified
† Summer visitor

Table II   Total figures of species and pairs of birds breeding at Kingley Vale (separate figures for passerines and summer visitors)

All birds	67	68	69	70	71	72	73	74	75	76	77
Total no. of species	40	37	41	38	42	41	43	40	43	42	39
Total no. of pairs	350	324	311	300	318	336	306	279	246	280	270
Passerines											
Total no. of species	32	29	31	30	32	29	27	28	30	29	29
Total no. of pairs	298	272	257	241	250	268	238	216	189	223	213
Percentage of the total of all birds	85	85	83	80	79	80	78	77	77	80	79
Summer visitors											
Total no. of species	9	9	9	9	10	9	8	8	9	10	9
Total no. of pairs	55	62	47	47	42	45	36	42	21	45	40
Percentage of the total of all birds	16	19	15	16	13	13	11	15	9	16	15

Table III   Breeding birds at Kingley Vale in order of their frequency

Species	*Average number*	*Percentage*
Chaffinch	34.3	11.33
Robin	31.3	10.33
Pigeon	30.0	10.00
Blackbird	23.5	7.83
Wren	20.1	6.7
Dunnock	15.9	5.3
Pheasant	15.7	5.2
Coal tit	12.6	4.2
Willow warbler	11.0	3.66
Great tit	10.8	3.6
Whitethroat	9.7	3.23
Yellowhammer	8.9	2.96
Goldcrest	7.9	2.63

Species	Average number	Percentage
Bullfinch	7.2	2.4
Chiffchaff	6.5	2.16
Song thrush	6.2	2.06
Blue tit	6.1	2.03
Blackcap	5.8	1.93
Nightingale	3.5	1.16
Greenfinch	3.3	1.1
Green woodpecker	3.0	1.0
Mistle thrush	2.4	.8
Marsh tit	2.3	.76
Linnet	2.3	.76
Grey partridge	2.0	.66
Cuckoo	2.0	.66
Turtle dove	1.8	.6
Lesser whitethroat	1.8	.6
Jay	1.5	.5
Long-tailed tit	1.5	.5
Tawny owl	1.3	.43
Carrion crow	1.3	.43
Starling	1.2	
Woodcock	1.1	.36
Kestrel	.9	.3
Jackdaw	.8	.26
Tree pipit	.8	.26
Lapwing	.7	.23
Skylark	.7	.23
Garden warbler	.7	.23
Magpie	.6	.2
Nuthatch	.6	.2
Meadow pipit	.5	.16
Sparrowhawk	.4	.13
Stockdove	.4	.13
Great spotted woodpecker	.4	.13
Goldfinch	.4	.13
Red-legged partridge	.3	.1
Golden pheasant	.3	.1
Nightjar	.3	.1
Barn owl	.2	.06
Little owl	.1	.03
Long-eared owl	.1	.03
Treecreeper	.1	.03
Grasshopper warbler	.1	.03
Spotted flycatcher	.1	.03

Table IV Territories chosen by birds breeding at Kingley Vale in the different habitat types during the succession from grassland to mature woodland, 1967-77

Species	Open grassland	Yew/oak islands and scrub	Young yew wood	Middle-aged yew wood	Mature yew/ash wood
Non-passerines					
Sparrowhawk				x	
Kestrel				x	
Red-legged partridge	x				
Grey partridge	x				
Pheasant	x	x	x	x	x

Species	Open grassland	Yew/oak islands and scrub	Young yew wood	Middle-aged yew wood	Mature yew/ash wood
Golden pheasant					x
Lapwing	x				
Woodcock		x			
Woodpigeon		x	x	x	x
Stockdove					x
† Turtle dove		x			
† Cuckoo		x		x	
Barn owl					x
Little owl		x			
Tawny owl		x	x	x	x
Long-eared owl			x		
† Nightjar			x		
Green woodpecker		x			x
Great spotted woodpecker		x			
Passerines					
Skylark	x				
Tree pipit			x		
Meadow pipit	x				
Jay		x	x	x	x
Magpie			x	x	
Jackdaw					x
Carrion crow		x	*	x	x
Wren		x	*	x	x
Dunnock		x	*	x	x
† Grasshopper warbler		x			
† Garden warbler		x			
† Blackcap		x		*	x
† Whitethroat		x			
† Lesser whitethroat		x			
† Willow warbler		x			
† Chiffchaff		x		*	x
Goldcrest		x		x	x
† Spotted flycatcher		x			
Robin		x	x	x	x
† Nightingale		x			
Blackbird		x	x	x	x
Song thrush		x		x	x
Mistle thrush		x		x	x
Marsh tit		x			x
Blue tit		x			x
Coal tit		x	x	x	x
Great tit		x	*	x	x
Long-tailed tit		x			
Nuthatch					x
Treecreeper		x			
Chaffinch		x	x	x	x
Bullfinch		x		x	x
Greenfinch		x		x	x
Goldfinch		x			
Linnet		x			
Corn bunting	—		—	—	—
Yellowhammer		x			
Starling					x

* Bird bred in this area although it is not its usual habitat

† Summer visitor

List of butterflies found at Kingley Vale, 1976-7
(as a result of the Butterfly Monitoring Scheme, under the aegis of the Institute of Terrestrial Ecology)

Total transect contacts	*1976*	*1977*
Brimstone	220	241
Brown argus	73	6
Chalkhill blue	26	11
Comma	40	6
Common blue	815	70
Dark green fritillary	148	42
Dingy skipper	141	25
Green hairstreak	25	12
Green-veined white	1	4
Grizzled skipper	126	65
Hedge brown	960	360
Holly blue	16	19
Large skipper	75	5
Large white	43	23
Marbled white	0	0
Meadow brown	3599	3425
Orange tip	3	6
Painted lady	1	2
Peacock	63	22
Pearl-bordered fritillary	8	
Purple emperor	1	
Purple hairstreak	2	
Red admiral	15	2
Ringlet	74	21
Small copper	327	123
Small heath	899	149
Small pearl-bordered fritillary	22	2
Small skipper	260	177
Small tortoiseshell	38	14
Small white	175	158
Speckled wood	89	21
Wall brown	146	9
White admiral	8	2
Total	8439	5022

List of moths found to date at Kingley Vale

This list is an amalgamation of information, including that received from Major Phillips, Mr Haes (Sussex Wildlife Recording Group) and Mr Pickering who was given a permit to examine night-flying moths. It must be understood that it can only represent a sample of the moths that are to be found on the reserve.

Sphingidae (Hawkmoths)

Sphinx ligustri	Privet hawkmoth
Laothoë populi	Poplar hawkmoth
Deilephila elpenor	Elephant hawkmoth
Deilephila porcellus	Small elephant hawkmoth
Hemaris tityus	Narrow-bordered bee hawkmoth
Macroglossum stellatarum	Humming bird hawkmoth

Notodontidae (Prominents)

Cerura vinula	Puss moth
Ptilodon capucina	Coxcomb prominent
Phalera bucephala	Buff-tip
Notodonta dromedarius	Iron prominent
Stauropus fagi	Lobster moth

Lymantriidae (Tussocks)

Origyria antiqua	Vapourer
Dasychira pudibunda	Pale tussock
Euproctis similis	Gold-tail

Thyatiridae (Thyatirids)

Habrosyne pyritoides	Buff arches
Thyatira batis	Peach blossom

Drepanidae (Hooktips)

Cilix glaucata	Chinese character
Laspeyria flexula	Beautiful hooktip
Drepana cultraria	Barred hooktip

Noctuidae (Noctuas or Owlets)

Noctua comes	Lesser yellow underwing
Noctua pronuba	Large yellow underwing
Lampra fimbriata	Broad-bordered yellow underwing
Triphaena ianthina	Lesser broad-bordered yellow underwing
Lycophotia porphyrea	True lover's knot
Polia nebulosa	Grey arches
Laconobia w-latinum	Light brocade
Ceramica psi	Broom moth
Mythimna conigera	Brown-line bright eye
Cucullia verbasci	Mullein shark
Acronicta aceris	Sycamore
Amphipyra tragopoginis	Mouse moth
Phologophora meticulosa	Angle shades
Euplexia lucipara	Small angle shades
Apamea monoglypha	Dark arches
Apamea lithoxylea	Light arches
Pseudoips fagana	Green silverlines
Scoliopterix libatrix	Herald
Autographia jota	Golden Y
Plusia gamma	Silver Y

Diachrysia chrysitis	Burnished brass
Callistege mi	Mother Shipton
Euclidia glyphica	Burnet companion
Mamestra brassicae	Cabbage moth
Ochropleura plecta	Flame shoulder
Eremobia ochroleuca	Dusky sallow
Noctua primulae	Ingrailed clay
Leucania lythargyria	The clay
Leucania pallens	Common wainscot
Leucania impura	Smoky wainscot
Unca triplasia	The spectacle
Melanchra persicariae	Dot moth
Diarsia brunnea	Purple clay
Axylia putris	The flame
Amanthes c-nigrum	Setaceous hebrew character
Cosmia trazezina	The dun-bar
Apemia secalis	Common rustic
Caradrina morpheus	Mottled rustic
Tholera cespitis	Hedge rustic
Agrotis exclamationis	Heart and dart

Lasiocampidae (Lackeys)

Malacosoma neustria	The lackey
Hypena proboscidalis	The snout

(Eggars)

Philudoria potatoria	The drinker
Gastropacha quercifolia	The lappet

Arctiidae (Tiger moths)

Spilosoma lubricipeda	White ermine
Phragmatobia fuliginosa	Ruby tiger
Tyria jacobaea	Cinnabar
Parasemia plantaginis	Wood tiger

Geometridae (Geometers)

Alsophila aescularia	March moth
Hemithea aestivaria	Common emerald
Hemithea chrysopresaria	Small emerald
Timandra griseata	Blood vein
Scopula lactata	Cream wave
S. bisetata	Small fan-footed wave
Idaea aversata	Riband wave

Geometridae: Laurentiinae (Carpets)

Anaitis plagiata	The treble-bar
Xanthorhoe montanata	Silver ground carpet
Scopteryx bipunctaria	Chalk carpet
Scopteryx chenopodiata	Shaded broad-bar
Camptogramma bilineata	Yellow shell
Horisime tersata	Fern moth
Melanthia procellata	Pretty chalk carpet
Operophtera brumata	Winter moth
Mesoleuca albicillata	Beautiful carpet
Hydriomena furcata	July highflyer
Ematurga atomaria	Heath carpet

Geometridae: Laureutiinae (Pugs)

Eupithica pulcellata	Foxglove pug

Eupithica centaureata	Lime-speck pug
Chloroclystis coronata	V-pug
Geometridae: Ennominae	
Abraxas grossulariata	Magpie moth
Campaea margaritata	Light emerald
Opisthograptis inteolata	Brimstone moth
Pseudopanthera macularia	Speckled yellow
Ourapteryx sambucaria	Swallow-tailed moth
P. transversata	Dark umber
Biston betularia	Peppered moth
Ectropis biundulata	The engrailed
Selenia bilunaria	Early thorn
H. vitalba	Small waved umber
Semothisa clathrata	Latticed heath
Cossidae (Goat and leopard moths)	
Zeuzera pyrina	Leopard moth
Zygaenidae (Burnets and foresters)	
Adscita statices	Green forester
Zygaena trifolii	Five-spot burnet
Zygaena filipendulae	Six-spot burnet
Sesiidae (Clearwings)	
Bembecia scopigera	Six-belted clearwing
Pyralidae (Pyralids)	
Crambus nemorella	
Crambus perlella	
Agriphilla sp.	
Thisanotia chrysonuchella	
Pyrusta purpuralis	Common crimson and gold
Pleuroptya ruralis	Mother of pearl
Myelois cribrella	Thistle ermine
Pterophoridae (Plume moths)	
Pterophorus tridactyla	Thyme-plume moth
Alucita hexadactyla	Many-plume moth
Micropterigidae	
Micropterix thunbergella	
Micropterix calthella	
Incurvidae (Long-horned moths)	
Adela viridella	Green longhorn
Nemophora degeerella	
Adela reamurella	
Lampronia rubiella	
Nepticuloidea	
Nepticula sp.	
Stigmella sp.	

List of other insects found on Kingley Vale

During the last two decades surveys by a number of groups and individuals have indicated that Sussex has an outstanding natural history, possibly the richest of any of our southern counties. Even today only a few groups of animals and plants are being studied in detail, so there seemed a real need for more complete investigation, at least of selected areas, by experienced field naturalists. For this reason a small group of observers have formed themselves into the West Sussex Wildlife Recording Group (Executive Secretary, E. C. M. Haes, B.Sc.). Their aim is not to compete with existing societies but to provide additional help for such societies where needed and to make detailed studies of sites which are obviously rich in wildlife. Kingley Vale and Bow Hill make up one such area and the group intends to complete a detailed investigation of the site. When sufficient data has been obtained it is hoped to publish the results in the form of a booklet, which should be a valuable complement to the present work.

The following list is extracted from data already collected by the group over the previous ten years. As such it comprises, in many instances, only a few of the more distinctive and noticeable species. Invertebrates only are listed as other groups are covered elsewhere in the book.

Thysanura (Bristle tails)
Dilta sp.

Orthoptera (Grasshoppers, Crickets and Bush-crickets)
Gryllidae
Gryllus campestris*   Field cricket*
Tettigoniidae
Meconema thalassinum   Oak bush-cricket
Pholidoptera griseoaptera   Dark bush-cricket
Leptophyes punctatissima   Speckled bush-cricket
Acrididae
Gomphocerippus rufus   Rufous grasshopper
Stenobothrus lineatus   Stripe-winged grasshopper
Omocestus viridulus   Common green grasshopper
O. rufipes   Woodland grasshopper
Chorthippus brunneus   Field grasshopper
C. parallelus   Meadow grasshopper
Tetrigidae
Tetrix undulata   Common ground-hopper

Dictyoptera (Cockroaches)
Blattidae
Ectobius lapponicus   Dusky cockroach
E. pallidus   Tawny cockroach

Dermaptera (Earwigs)
Forficulidae
Forficula auricularia   Common earwig

Odonata (Dragonflies and Damselflies)
Zygoptera
Coenagrion puella   Common coenagrion
Enellagma cyathigerum   Common blue damselfly
Ischnura elegans   Common ischnura
Anisoptera
Aeshna mixta   'Scarce' aeshna
Sympetrum striolatum   Common sympetrum

Hemiptera (Bugs)
Acanthosomidae
Acanthosoma haemorrhoides   Hawthorn shield-bug
Pentatomidae
Palomina prasina   Stink bug
Picnomerus bidens
Dolycoris baccarum   Sloebug

---

* It is proposed to introduce native stock of this dangerously rare species.

Lygaidae
Stygnocoris pedestris
Nabidae
Nabus rugosus   Common damsel bug
Miridae
Lygus rugilipennis   Tarnished plantbug
Tingidae
Tingis cardui   Thistle racebug

Homoptera (Hoppers and Aphids)
Cercopidae
Cercopis vulnerata   Red and black froghopper
Philaeneus spumarius   Common froghopper
Cicadellidae
Limnotettix striola
Membracidae
Centrotus cornutus   Horned leaf-hopper
Coleoptera (Beetles)
Carabidae (Ground beetles)
Cicindella campestris   Green tiger beetle
Carabus violaceus   Violet ground beetle
Bembidion lampros
Harpalus aeneus
Amara aenea
Pseudophonus pubescens
Staphalinidae (Rove beetles)
Ocypus olens   Devil's coach horse
Lampyridae
Lampyris noctiluca   Glow-worm
Cantharidae
Podabrus alpinus
Cantharis rustica   Sailor beetle
Rhagonycha fulva   Soldier beetle

Drilidae
Drilus flavescens
Malachiidae
Malachius bipustulatus
Elateridae (Click beetles)
Athous haemorrhoidalis
Agriotes obscura
Brachylacon murinus
Coccinellidae (Ladybirds)
Thea 22-punctata
Adalia 10-punctata   Ten spot ladybird
A. bipunctata   Two spot ladybird
Coccinella septempunctata   Seven spot ladybird
Oedemerida
Oedemera nobilis
Pyrochroidae
Pyrochroa seraticornis   Red-headed cardinal beetle
Chrysomelidae
Timarcha tenebricosa   Bloody-nosed beetle
T. goettingensis   Lesser bloody-nosed beetle
Cryptocephelus aureolus
Cassida rubiginosa   Thistle tortoise beetle
Scarabaeidae (Dung beetles and chafers)
Geotrupes stercorarius   Lousy watchman
Cerambycidae (Long-horn beetles)
Clytus arietis   Wasp beetle

Strangalia maculata
S. melanura

Diptera (True flies)
Syrphidae (Hover flies)
Leucozona lucorum
Xanthogramma citrofasciatum
Syrphus umbellatum
Scatophagidae
Scatophaga stercorarium   Dung fly
Sarcophagidae
Sarcophaga carnaria   Flesh fly
Empidae
Empis tesselata

Hymenoptera
Pompiloidae (Spider-hunting wasps)
Priocnemis exaltata
Arachnospila spissa
A. anceps
Vespoidea (Solitary and social wasps)
Vespula rufa
Dolichovespula sylvestris
Sphecoidea (Solitary wasps)
Pemphredon schuckardi
Psenulus concolor
Ectemnius lapidarius
E. lituratus
E. continuus
Apoidea (Bees)
Hylaeus annularis
H. communis
Halictus rubicundis
H. tumulorum
Lasioglossum leucozonulum
L. calciatum
L. albipes
Andrena haemorrhoa
A. bicolor
A. subopaca
Melitta haemorrhoidalis
Nomada marshamella
Ceratina cyanea
Hoplitis claviventris
Bombus terrestris
B. lucorum
B. lapidarius   Bumble bees
B. ruderarius
B. pascuorum
B. humilis
Psithyrus campestris
Apis mellifera   Honey bee

Arachnida (Spiders)
Gnaphosidae
Zelotes latreillei
Thomisidae (Crab spiders)
Diaea dorsata
Misumena vatia
Xysticus cristatus
Philodromus histrio
P. aoreolus

Salticidae (Jumping spiders)
Ballus depressus
Evarcha arcuata
Euophrys frontalis
Lycosidae (Wolf spiders)
Lycosa sp.
Tarentula cuneata
Trochosa terricola
Pisauridae
Pisaura mirabilis
Agelenidae
Agelina labyrinthica
Argiopidae (Orb-web spiders)
Araneus diadematus
A. quadratus   Garden spider
A. cucurbitinus
Zygiella atrica

Numbers of visitors to Kingley Vale, 1973–7

	Museum: general public		Museum: school parties or groups		Total
	Visitors	Days open	Individuals	No. of groups	visitors
1973	3563	42	1338	38	4901
1974	4020	42	1282	39	5302
1975	3754	49	1501	39	5255
1976	3331	35	1768	48	5099
1977	3371	40	1617	47	4988

Bibliography

Andersen, J., 'Analysis of Danish roedeer populations based upon extermination of the total stock', *Dan. Rev. Game Biol.* 2 (1953) 127–55.

Ascham, Roger, 'Toxophilus', 1545 (in Lowe, pp. 114, 131).

Badger Act (H.M.S.O., 1973) ch. 57.

Brady, John, *Clavis Calendaria* (in Lowe, p. 99).

Browne, Thomas, *Hydriotaphia, or Urne Burials*, 1658 (in Lowe, pp. 97, 167).

Caesar, Julius, *De Bello Gallico* (in Lowe, p. 136).

Caxton, William, 'Directions for Keeping Feasts all the Year' (in Lowe, p. 100).

Clements, E. D., 'The National Badger Survey in Sussex' (in Tittensor *et al.*, p. 38).

Coote, Henry, *The Romans in Britain*, 1878 (in Lowe, p. 98).

Cornish, V., *The Churchyard Yew and Immortality* (London, 1946).

Deer Act (H.M.S.O., 1963) ch. 36.

Edlin, H. L., *The Living Forest* (Thames and Hudson, 1958).

Elwes, H. J. and Henry, A. H., *The Trees of Great Britain and Ireland* (Edinburgh, 1906).

Evelyn, John, *Sylva: Discourse on Trees*, 1664 (in Lowe).

Gardeners' Chronicle, 1881 (in Lowe, pp. 139–40).

Gerard, John, *The Herbale or General Historie of Plantes*, 1636 (in Lowe, p. 138).

Godwin, H., *The History of the British Flora* (Cambridge University Press, 1956).

Hansard, G. A., *The Book of Archery*, 1841 (in Lowe, p. 104).

Heit, C. E., 'Testing and growing seeds of popular taxus foms', *American Nurseryman* 129, 2 (1969) 10–11, 118–28.

Howarth, T. G., *South's British Butterflies* (Warne, 1973).

Hudson, W. H., *Nature in Downland* (Dent, 1923).

Hutchinson, R., 'On the old and remarkable yew trees in Scotland', *Trans. Roy. Scot. Arb. Soc.* 12 (1890) 379–402.

International Bird Census Committee, 'Recommendations for an international standard for a mapping method in bird census work', *Bird Study* 16 (1969) 249–55.

Kingley Vale National Nature Reserve Nature Trail (pub. by Nature Conservancy Council, available at the reserve).

Loudon, John C., *Arboretum Britannicum: Encyclopedia of Trees*, 1838 (in Lowe, pp. 109, 132, 150).

——*Magazine of Natural History*, 1836 (in Lowe, pp. 109, 132, 150).

Longman's Magazine, 1883 (in Lowe).

Lowe, J., *The Yew Trees of Gt. Britain and Ireland* (London, 1897).

Magazine of Natural History (1836).

'Management Plan – Kingley Vale National Nature Reserve' (Nature Conservancy, unpub. doc., 1959, revised 1965).

Medical Times and Gazette, 1830 (in Lowe, pp. 139–40).

National Parks and Access to the Countryside Act (H.M.S.O., 1949) ch. 97, sec. 15.

New Planter's Kalender (in Lowe, p. 150).

Newbould, P. J., 'The Age and Structure of the Yew Wood at Kingley Vale' (unpub. report, 1960).

Papworth, D. S., 'A review of the dangers of Warfarin poisoning to animals other than rodents', *Roy. Soc. Health Journal* 78 (1958) 52–60.

'Pest Infestation Control', Laboratory Report 1971–3 (M.A.F.F., A.D.A.S., H.M.S.O., 1975; report for 1974–6 in press).

Pollard, E., Elias, D. O., Shelton, M. J. and Thomas, J. A., 'A method of assessing the abundance of butterflies in Monk's Wood National Nature Reserve', *Entomologists Gazette* 26 (1973).

Ratcliffe, D. (ed.), *A Nature Conservation Review* (Nature Conservancy Council, 1977).

Rowe, J. J., 'The Grey Squirrel and its Control in Great Britain', Forestry Commission Leaflet no. 56 (1973).

Simms, E., *Woodland Birds*, New Naturalist Series 52 (Collins, 1971).

Southern, H. N. (ed.), *The Handbook of British Mammals* (Blackwell Scientific Publications, 1964).

Taylor, J. C., Lloyd, H. G. and Shillits, J. F., 'Experiments with Warfarin for Grey Squirrel control', *Ann. Appl. Biol.* 61 (1968) 312–21.

Tegetmeir, W. B., *Pheasants* (London, 1881).

Thomas, A. S., 'Changes in vegetation since the advent of myxomatosis', *J. Ecol.* 48 (1960) 287–306.

Tittensor, A. M. *et al.* (eds), *The Sussex Mammal Report*, Sussex Trust for Nature Conservation Biennial Report (1970–71).

Williamson, K. and Homes, R. C., 'Methods and preliminary results of the Common Bird Census 1962–3', *Bird Study* 11 (1964) 240–56.

Williamson, Richard and Williamson, K., 'The bird community of yew woodland at Kingley Vale, Sussex', *British Birds* 66 (Jan 1963) 12–63.

Wood, D. A. and Phillipson, J., 'Squirrel poison hoppers', *Biol. Conservation* (Feb 1977).

Watt, A. S., 'Yew communities of the South Downs', *J. Ecol.* 14 (1926) 382–316

Recommended further reading

Burton, J., *The Oxford Book of Insects* (Oxford University Press, 1968).

Haes, E. C. M., *Natural History of Sussex* (Harvester Press, 1977).

Lousley, J. E., *Wild Flowers of Chalk and Limestone*, 2nd ed., New Naturalist Series 16 (Collins, 1969).

McClintock, D. and Fitter, R. S. R., *The Pocket Guide to Wild Flowers* (Collins, 1956).

Summerhayes, V. S., *Wild Orchids of Britain*, New Naturalist Series 21 (Collins, 1951).

Sussex Bird Report, Sussex Ornithological Soc. (annually).

Index

Numbers in italics refer to illustrations